PRAISE FOR 6 TO 6

"On par with Denis Johnson, John Fante and even Hemingway, it's sad this masterful writer isn't getting the attention he deserves. His characterization of the Southwest is austere, blinding, and directly beneath the sun." — Jon Bennett

"Schneider is the master of the oddball. He takes us along for the ride with the drunks, the infirmed, and the gangsters that have piled into the back of his cab, many of whom don't even know their own destination. Hernia trusses are the order of the day as you bust a gut laughing at the twisted humor and ingenuity that is Mather Schneider's storytelling. *6 to 6* is a diabolical memoir that raises the bar on writing today. The road to hell is paved with dark, cynical humor, and I want to be riding shotgun in Schneider's cab on the way down." — Hugh Blanton

"Mather Schneider is a polarizing figure: some love him, some hate him, but few could hate his writing, which regularly digs deep, past all the bullshit, to the hidden souls of the flawed characters he writes about, showing unexpected beauty behind their endless life dilemmas. He is an authentic writer of the low life that has spent most of his working life as a cab driver developing his writing skills, gathering endless material along the way. *6 to 6* by Mather Schneider is a veteran writer at the height of his powers." — Brenton Booth, author of *Bash the Keys Until They Scream*

"Mr. Mather has composed a gritty collection that hits harder than a tube sock full of ball bearings. Read at your own risk." — Brian Fugett, *Zygote in My Coffee*

ALSO BY MATHER SCHNEIDER

6 TO 6

MATHER SCHNEIDER

Sheridan, WY
Terror House Press
2020

This is a work of nonfiction. While all of the characters and events depicted in this book are real, names and identifying details have been changed.

ISBN 978-1-951897-22-2

EDITOR

Matt Forney (mattforney.com)

LAYOUT AND COVER DESIGN

Matt Lawrence (mattlawrence.net)

Excerpts of this book were published, in somewhat different form, by *Terror House Magazine*. The author would like to thank *Terror House* for their support.

TERROR HOUSE PRESS, LLC

terrorhousepress.com

TABLE OF CONTENTS

On Monday, I drove down the road

and smashed my wheels in a hole.

On Tuesday, I drove down the road

and smashed my wheels in the hole.

On Wednesday, I drove down the road

and smashed my wheels in the hole.

On Thursday, I drove down the road

and swerved around the hole.

On Friday, I drove down the road

and swerved around the hole.

On Saturday, I drove down the road

and swerved around the hole.

On Sunday, I drove down a different road.

TRAVELING MERCIES

She got Mother-Theresa-like into my cab in her brown dress and said:

"To Saint Augustine Cathedral, on Broadway."

Saint Augustine was on the other side of town; at least a $30 ride. Praise the Lord.

"Nice morning, huh?" I said.

"Oh, yes," she said. "Another blessed day."

"Couldn't agree more."

"How long you been driving a cab?"

"Seems like since the world began."

"You must like it."

I didn't say anything to that.

Then she asked me: "Do you know what traveling mercies are?"

"I think I saw them on YouTube once."

"Traveling mercies are a gift from God that can be given from one person to another."

"Huh."

"Well," she said, "if you will permit me, I would like to bestow upon you some traveling mercies."

"This isn't gonna hurt, is it?" I said.

"No. It will calm your soul."

"All right, then."

1

She closed her eyes and took a deep breath and said, "I bestow upon you many traveling mercies for this day and the days to follow."

"That's it?" I said.

"That's pretty much it," she said.

"Okay. Thanks."

"You're welcome. Everyone deserves some traveling mercies. It's a crazy world out there."

"Amen, sister."

NEXT TIME, TAKE SKYLINE

Dispatch sent me to a house in the Tucson foothills. It was a typical foothills community full of upper class false-adobe houses all painted the same sallow desert tan. No real color was allowed by the neighborhood ordinance. It was 111 degrees and there hadn't even been a cloud in four days.

When I arrived in my cab, I heard loud music inside the house. I didn't see anybody. No phone number had been provided. I got out of the cab and knocked on the door several times. A man grunted: "RIGHT OUT!" I waited on the sunny driveway and looked at my watch: 2:15 PM.

The door opened and a Rottweiler leaped out at me. A man inside caught the dog by the scruff of the neck.

"You son of a BITCH!" he screamed and kicked the dog viciously back inside.

He was Hispanic, around 50, black hair slicked back into a tiny, perfectly tight ponytail. He wore sunglasses, a brown wool sports jacket, new blue jeans, and walnut-colored dress shoes. And he was BUILT. Not tall, but wide. He had a confidence. He held a glass of beer and walked toward the cab.

In the cab, he said: "I'm Carlos."

"Matt."

"I heard about Big John," Carlos said.

Big John had been a cab driver for many years. He had died a few weeks before of a kidney infection. He had complained about pain for days, but he wouldn't go to the doctor; he said he didn't have the money. One day, he drove his cab to the hospital and walked into the emergency room. He was dead seven hours later.

"A friend of yours?" I said.

"Of course," Carlos said. "He was my driver for ten years. I've been... out of town. I just heard about his death. Big John was a good man."

I had never liked Big John much.

"Where we headed?" I said.

Carlos looked at me as if he had been offended.

"Craycroft and Pima."

The east side. That meant at least $35 on the meter.

"You want me to take the freeway?" I said.

"Whatever you want."

"Or maybe Skyline Drive?"

"Either one."

I sat there a moment. I was nervous. I was just a middle-aged guy with a studio apartment; I didn't want any trouble. Carlos took a handgun out of his coat pocket and sat it on the seat beside him.

"I'll take the freeway," I said.

Carlos had cans of beer in the pockets of his sports jacket. He finished his glass and took a can out and filled it again. He was perfectly shaved, except for a little hair under the middle of his lower lip.

A piece of rubber tire came upon us on the highway. I swerved to miss it and Carlos nearly spilled his beer.

"Take it easy," he said.

"Sorry."

Halfway there, Carlos said, "Next time, take Skyline."

Carlos told me to pull into the parking lot of a pawnshop. He got out slowly and strutted into the store. He stayed inside for at least 20 minutes. My palms were wet. *I should leave, I should leave,* I thought. Carlos had taken his gun with him.

After a while, I got out of the cab and looked in the glass doors of the

4

pawn shop. At that moment, Carlos came out, almost hitting me in the nose with the door.

"I see how you are," Carlos said.

"Just checking my hair," I told him.

"I need a beer," Carlos said. "Take me to the south side."

The south side was another 20 minutes away, and once we got there, he wanted me to go to a gas station, where he bought a 12-pack of beer. Then he instructed me to park in an alley looking out onto the street, right next to a Mexican guy selling corn out of the back of his truck. The corn nearly steamed in its husks sitting there in boxes in the sun. The meter clicked more slowly as we sat. I watched it like the doomsday clock.

Carlos drank his beer.

I turned around and looked at him.

"Can I ask a question?" I said. Carlos nodded and lifted his hand.

"What exactly are we doing?" I said.

Carlos smiled and shook his head.

"In life, you must be flexible," he said.

"But what is our ultimate destination?"

"You'll have to ask God that question, my friend. Just drive."

He wanted me to drive when he told me to drive and to turn where he told me to turn and to listen when he talked. Carlos measured my reactions.

"You have a girlfriend?" Carlos asked.

"No."

"Are you a man, or what?" he said.

"I think so."

"I have four girlfriends," Carlos said. "One in New York, one in Brazil, and two in Mexico."

"That's a lot."

"Not really," he said.

"They like the money," I said.

5

"No!" Carlos said. "It's more than the money."

"All right."

Carlos wanted the music turned up. Then he talked in whispers.

"A man needs to have some fun once in a while," he said.

I knew what he meant.

"You know what I mean?" he said.

"Yes."

"What?"

"YES!"

The whole thing was some kind of test.

"Can you keep a secret?" Carlos said.

"Sure."

I didn't want any secrets, I'd had enough of secrets. My heart was racing and I was sweating all over. My fear was mixed with anger.

"I mean," he said, "you know where I live, you know all this about me."

"You haven't told me anything."

"I'm not stupid."

"I didn't say you were stupid."

"I don't want to wake up with an ice pick in the back of my neck," Carlos said. "You have to be careful. Just like driving this cab around, you never know who you're going to pick up."

"True."

"Can you keep your mouth shut is what I'm asking you," Carlos said.

"If I have to."

"One day a man might come up to you," Carlos said.

"Yes?"

"This man may look just like me, this man may even claim to be me. What will you tell him?"

"Nothing, Carlos."

"Pull over here."

6

We sat on 12th Avenue, which was Carlos's street. He "ran" it. One of the perks of running a street was that he never had to pay for anything and could supposedly walk up to any woman he saw and take her to a hotel.

It was all about something he called "protection." Jim had been his driver for nearly ten years. Apparently, Carlos was never in Tucson long enough to have his own car, so he used Jim. Old Jim was driving his cab around Hell right about then, which was probably not much hotter than Tucson.

"Nobody's gonna take care of you," Carlos said. "You've got to take care of yourself. A man's got to take care of himself, you know what I mean?"

"Yes."

"Look around you," he said. "That guy selling corn out of the back of his goddamned truck back there? He's got an old lady at home and four kids, man. Who's gonna take care of them?"

"I don't know."

"Me!" Carlos said. "Nobody else is gonna do it! I take care of them. They are like my children. I would do anything for them. I mean, sometimes you gotta kick ass, but that's just how it goes."

He held out his right arm and flexed his biceps.

"Go ahead," he said, "feel it. 18 fucking inches."

"Wow."

Carlos looked at me. He liked me, but he didn't like me.

"You don't understand anything, do you?"

"I'm not from this world," I said.

Carlos laughed. He shook my hand about 20 times and said he wanted me to be his new driver. My hand was still sweaty, and when Carlos let go, he wiped his hand on his jeans and smiled viciously.

Intimidation vibrated from Carlos. He sat back there, ensconced in malignant ego, completely full of himself, ready to kill at any moment, or ready to die. He was a man you just did not fuck with. And his gun sat there the whole time.

The next part of the afternoon was spent going to various places. He kept barking at me.

"Pull over there! Not here, there! Do what I tell you!"

At one point, I pulled the cab over outside of a little taco stand. I told Carlos he was wearing me out and that I was tired of his mouth. My fear had been exhausted and I was just plain pissed. Plus, I was hungry. Carlos looked at me with shock. I figured I was done for. But Carlos softened. He grinned and patted me on the shoulder.

"You have some balls after all, my friend," he said.

After that, he was quiet and more polite.

We stopped at many pawnshops and bars so Carlos could collect protection money or just throw his weight around. He was never in these places more than a few minutes. Sometimes he returned slightly winded or with a layer of perspiration on his upper lip. Other times I heard loud voices from inside the buildings, and one time a muffled gunshot. I sat behind the wheel and stared through my sunglasses into the sunshine, at the palms and cactus and dusty alleys. I just could not leave. Carlos knew what company I worked for and unless I was willing to leave the city, I was afraid Carlos would find me if I just drove off and left him.

Outside of one Mexican restaurant, there were four Mexican musicians unloading their musical instruments from a truck. Four old Mexican men, dressed like farmers. They were preparing to play in the restaurant.

"Stop the car," Carlos said.

He got out and walked over to the musicians, snapping something in Spanish. They jumped like Satan's jesters. Carlos walked back and climbed into the cab, leaving the door open. The windows were down. The musicians scrambled over and stood right next to the cab. Carlos named a song and they exploded into it. They played their hearts out. The instruments that they strummed and pounded were held together by duct tape and carpentry nails, too beat up and old to even interest a pawn shop.

They were more scared than I was. They knew this Carlos. I could see it on their faces. They were all sweating in the afternoon sun. Everybody was sweating except Carlos. There was no joy in that music, only fear of hitting a wrong note. After about five songs, Carlos tired of them, waved them off. Not a dime tip.

8

When he walked out of yet another pawnshop, he told me he would be staying there for a while and that I was free to leave. I had been held hostage for over four hours.

"Whatever you want," I said.

"I'm a man," Carlos said. "I do what I want."

The rest of his 12-pack of beer sat on the floor of the cab.

"You want your beer?"

"Fuck the beer."

"All right."

"You're my driver, right?" Carlos said. "You will take me here and there, sometimes?"

"Sure, Carlos."

There didn't seem to be anything else to say, no way out of it.

The fare was $180. Carlos took out an inch-thick fold of bills and handed me the exact amount. Then he made theatrics about giving me a $5 tip.

"I always pay my debts," he said. "Remember that."

He said he would be calling and warned me again about keeping my mouth shut. I drove out of there with my heart beating like a rabbit's. I drove around until I found a shady spot on the north side of town and sat there, thinking about those musicians, their strained smiles in the hot sun, their long, bony, brown fingers plucking the guitar strings, tapping the drum, blowing the horn. The lone singer lifting his head to open his throat.

SUICIDE LANE

Yesterday on Grant Road, I got behind a 4Runner SUV, blue-gray, dirty, maybe ten years old. It was going slow in the fast lane. Rush hour. I finally got a gap in the slow lane and put my blinker on to pass it. Then the fucker went into the slow lane right in front of me, blocked me again! Shit fire! All the cars in the fast lane poured through like wasps through a knothole.

In a mile, I finally got a gap in the fast lane and jumped back in there and passed the 4Runner. I glanced over: a woman driving, putting her makeup on, smearing it all around her face, oblivious to the chaos around her, blessed with natural blinders. Good Lord Almighty!

Then today, I got on Grant Road again, like a moron, and I swear to God I found myself behind the very same 4Runner. Tucson is a city of a million people. An indifferent universe my fat, white, hairy ass! She was again going 10 MPH below the limit. When I managed to get past her, I looked over and this time she was eating something out of a paper sack.

My soul. She was eating my soul.

She was enjoying it, and would not turn her head to meet my stare.

MORENCI IN MY REAR-VIEW MIRROR

She exhaled marijuana smoke into my cab when she got in and told me to take her to Tucson Medical Center.

"The E.R.?" I said. "You all right?"

"I'm fine, I'm going to visit my daughter."

She was fiftyish, short in stature with a rough but friendly face and dyed brown hair.

"My daughter's a mess," she said. "She's been sick since she was six years old. She's 25 now, four feet tall, and weighs 70 pounds. She's had cancer and one of her kidneys taken out and all kinds of shit. But she's a fighter."

"Poor thing, I'm sorry."

"Yeah. My son's fucked up too. Who knows why. He joined the army and came home last year and decided he was gonna beat me up. He said he had PTSD. Fuck, I got PMS, that's no fucking excuse! He was mean and nasty way before he ever went into the army. He was born a dick."

"Some people are that way, I guess."

"My son will never forgive me because his father got murdered. But hell, I didn't shoot him! His father pulled a gun on some guy and the guy shot him. Dumb bastard didn't even have any bullets in his gun when he pulled it...so of course nothing happened to the guy who killed him. I knew the guy who killed him. Morenci is a small town, mining town, that's where we're from."

"I been through there before."

13

"So you know, then?"

I had been to Morenci only once, on a long weekend drive. I saw the Morenci copper mine in the middle of the small town, the great pit with its spiraling roadways cut into the amber earth going all the way down to the bottom. I couldn't quite see the bottom of the mine from the road through town. I got out of my car and stood at the edge, but I still couldn't see the bottom. I had taken a long drive in the desert to escape the problems I was experiencing at that time and somehow I ended up in Morenci. Hundreds of people had died in that copper mine and I could almost hear the cries and echoes of the dead as I looked down into it.

"I remember the mine," I said. "There's an old drive-in movie theater, too, right? Out in the middle of nowhere in the desert?"

"Yeah, we had some good times out there."

The Morenci drive-in movie theater had been abandoned for years, left to the weeds and jackrabbits and cacti. A ghostly sight, out in the middle of the desert hills, one of those things you saw but didn't quite believe you saw. The small town of Morenci had never grown around it, always seeming to be slipping into the giant copper mine pit. The drive-through theater could be seen from the highway, the façade of the screen standing like a tremendous square sail that shook when the wind got strong. The old dilapidated snack bar hunched low and the rows of broken and bent microphones protruded like simple grave-markers out of the crumbling asphalt. The circular rows, or half-circular rows, within the parking lot where the cars used to park reminded me of the circular roadways that spiraled down into the copper mine pit. It was like an alien ruin, something from the imagination. Stories have filtered around for years of lights flickering from the big sail-like screen, of movies being played on it, silent movies with images that are impossible to define. Young people and drunks and desert hermits and Indians swear that the screen still lights up sometimes and shows movies that make no sense, like watching a giant television without your glasses and the sound turned off. One also hears stories of the parking lot filled with rows of vehicles of unknown makes and models, shadowy forms inside them, and of the cords to the microphones lifting and twisting of their own volition, like rattlesnakes.

"Funny thing," the woman said, "I picked him up one time while he was hitchhiking, the guy who killed my husband. Paul, his name was, we

14

called him Big Paul. It was raining and I saw some guy standing on the side of the road hitchhiking. I pulled my truck over and he gets in and son of a bitch if it wasn't Big Fucking Paul. He just looked at me and said, 'Hi Nancy. I sure am sorry about what happened to Mick.'"

"Mick was your husband?"

"Yeah. So what am I gonna say to that? 'It's okay,' I told him. Not really, but I said it anyway. Then a few years later, some guys got a hold of Big Paul and fucked him up. They cut his tongue out and his balls off and shot him like twelve times, left him in the desert. Cops found him out near that old drive-through."

"Oh my God."

"Yeah. That's when we moved to Tucson. We like it here."

"I like it here, too."

"Still, I miss Morenci sometimes. Small town. Everybody knows each other. I miss that sometimes."

"Yeah. I hear you."

We arrived at the hospital.

"Which entrance you want?" I said.

"Damn, she told me and now I forgot. Go that way."

I circled around the giant hospital grounds. It was always expanding, constantly under construction, a massive industrial medical complex that threatened to envelope the whole west side of Tucson, a macabre, theatrical catacombs.

"There, stop there," she said. "Shit, this ain't gonna be pretty. When I talked to my daughter on the phone, she said the doctors won't give her much for the pain on account of her only weighing 70 pounds. But this girl has a very high tolerance for the drugs, and she gets, how shall I say, 'grouchy' sometimes, and blames it on me. This might be a short visit; you gonna be in the area for a while?"

"Probably, give me a call if you want to go home."

"Okay."

I got out of the cab, walked around, and opened the door for her. She was fussing with her money and a handful of nondescript papers. Things

15

fell from her purse to the floor of the cab. She wore blue jean cut-offs and her legs were short and swollen and covered in black stubble.

"Here's my number," I said, and handed her my card.

She took the card and stuffed two twenties in my hand for a $30 fare. There exist people in this world who handle money like they don't know what to do with it, as if it's a foreign thing in their hands and they'd feel better to be rid of it.

"Thank you very much," I said.

She walked into the hospital.

She never did call for a ride home. I went home at five o'clock and my phone never rang. As I sat alone in my apartment, I couldn't get Nancy or that drive-through movie theater in the desert or the mine pit out of my head. I turned the television on, but it seemed to make no sense, and so I turned the sound down. I wished I had some marijuana to smoke, but the cab company that has employed me for, God, 17 years now tests my blood for that. It was possible Nancy's visit with her daughter went better than expected and she stayed at the hospital all night. It was possible she misplaced my card with my phone number on it or hitchhiked home or took the bus or even walked. You never knew.

A SPIRITUAL ADVENTURE

I am dispatched in my cab to one of Tucson's many "spiritual retreats." I feel my chakras squinching up as soon as I pull in. A line of pine trees leads into the "ashram area." The trees are watered artificially and suck God knows how much water from the aquifer, but it's pretty. I find "Meditation Abode Number 14," which looks as swank as a miniature Marriott. My passenger is a portly white woman around 60 years old wearing Birkenstocks and a Himalayan pashmina with what appears to be a mustard stain on the front. She gets in the cab.

"6565 Carondolet."

"Sure."

"Been driving a cab long?"

"Eight years."

"Oh, well, these are hard times."

"Yeah. Thanks."

"Are you going to take Speedway or Grant?"

"I was going to take Grant."

"Oh, I see..."

"You don't like Grant?"

"Well, Speedway is better."

"Grant has fewer stoplights."

"They have the same amount of stoplights."

"No, they don't."

"Yes, they do."

"Oh, I must not have noticed that after eight years driving a cab here."

"I'm very observant. But go ahead, take whatever street you want."

"So, what's this, an ashram?"

"It's a spiritual place. The people who live here are very spiritual."

"Is it expensive?"

"That's not important."

"True. Look, I'm taking Speedway."

"You can always learn something."

"I appreciate it."

"I'll teach you another thing: there's a secret way in."

"To the spirit?"

"No, to 6565 Carondolet."

"The marijuana dispensary?"

"Herbal clinic."

"Sorry."

"It's okay. Have you been there?"

"About 50 times. I remember when they opened it. It used to be a tire shop."

"Well, I'll teach you the back way in."

"Can't wait."

I drive a few miles down Speedway and take a right on Craycroft.

"Take a right on Craycroft."

"We're already on Craycroft."

"Good job."

When we arrive, I get into the left turn lane and sit there with my blinker on, waiting for the traffic to let me turn.

"Turn left here."

"You mean here?"

"Yes, turn left here."

"If you say so."

I turn left and head into the parking lot. There's a "main entrance" and a back entrance, both of which I've been aware of for years. The main entrance is where you are supposed to drop people off, and the back door is for the employees.

"So, you want the main entrance?"

"No! I'll teach you the secret entrance. Keep going."

"You mean there's another entrance?"

"Yes, it's not well-known."

"I'm trusting you now."

"Life is an adventure."

I pull up a few yards to the only other entrance.

"Surely you don't want me to go in here?"

"Yes, pull in."

I pull in and see the back door, cars parked in every spot.

"Pull right up there."

"You mean where it says NO PARKING?"

"Yes, right there. You learn something every day, don't you?"

"Do you know how much parking tickets cost in this town?"

"I don't drive."

She gets out and heads in.

I stand up and say, "Uh, pardon me, that will be $18."

"Oh, yes, your precious *money*," she says. She comes back to the cab and hands me some bills. There's a ten, a five, and some bill of foreign currency.

"What's this?" I say.

"My mistake; this is Tibetan money from my last trip. You've never been?"

"It's on the bucket list."

19

She finds three wadded up dollar bills and stuffs them in my hand.

"I'll be ready to go back home at two o'clock," she says.

"Just call the number," I say. "And pray someone answers."

I get out of there as the security guard rushes my way. Some guy cuts me off as I try to pull out onto Wilmot Street, probably stoned out of his gourd.

"Om," I say to myself. "Stay calm."

Suddenly, I have a craving for crawdad Pad Thai.

SONJA'S RING

Sonja is a big black lady, a sweetheart. Her body's falling apart at age 43: knees, back, innards. She can't drive anymore. She took my cab to work last week and she asked me if I would be her regular driver. She's a caregiver for an 80-year-old lady down on the south side, but she's the one who needs a caregiver. She only works on Sundays. It takes her a while to climb into the back seat, groaning in pain, nearly in tears.

"All, right, Matt, I'm in!" she says.

I get the cab moving.

"How's it going, Sonja?"

"Can't complain, no sir! God's been a-SHINING on ME! I won 30 bucks last night on the penny slots!"

"All right!"

"I think Martin was there, giving me luck."

"Martin?"

"My ex. God, he was such a slut! Men, you know? No offense! That motherfucker would fuck anything that came around. But I loved him. Still do. He was an alkie, too; what a shame. Dumb slut got the AIDS, but it was his liver that finally kilt him."

"You're just a loving person, Sonja."

"I even had me a couple of Bahama Mamas last night!"

"What's in those?"

"I have no idea, but they sure got my big black ass rollin'!"

The next week, she's moving even slower and more laboriously than before.

"You go to the casino last night, Sonja?"

"Naw, my son came over, do you know he brought me $40? I told him, you trying to give me a heart attack bringing me $40 out of the blue? Bless that boy."

"You stayed home?"

"Hell no! I went down to buy me some lotto tickets. Do you know that cashier was hitting on me? I must have been looking cute yesterday."

"Cuter than normal?"

"Oh, Matt, you are a doll! If you wasn't married, mmmm, hmmmm..."

"How'd those lotto tickets turn out?"

"Shit. Do you know while I was buying them tickets, some little ho in line behind me started giving me the business? Some little petite little thang! Oh, she thought she was something, gettin' all up on me like she was in some big hurry to get down to the strip-house and do her thang or some other skanky shit."

"Fucking people!"

"You know it, Matt! So I turns to her and I say, you don't want BIG SASSY to come out on your skinny little ass!"

"Who's Big Sassy?" I say.

"Big Sassy lives inside me. She used to come out all the time, back in my wild days. She don't come out much anymore."

"I wouldn't want to mess with Big Sassy."

"You got that right. Even Martin wouldn't mess with Big Sassy. The only one who ain't afraid of Big Sassy is my mama. But then, Mama's not afraid of nothin'."

"You live with your mother?"

"Yes, she took me in a few years ago when I got sick."

"Nice lady."

"You don't know my mama, ha ha! Naw, she's all right. But she keeps buying too much food. We got the freezer full and stuff's just falling out on the floor when you open it up. I told her, stop buyin' so much food, Mama, but she can't resist a sale. Just yesterday, she came home from Fry's and honked the horn. You KNOW when Mama honks the horn, she done bought a lot of groceries and needs some help carrying them in."

"You crack me up, Sonja."

"The Lord's been good to us."

***

Every week she's got a story and every time we laugh and every time she looks sicker and more tired.

The next week when I pick her up, she's telling me a story and stops short, says, "Shit!"

"What happened?"

"I just done lost my ring."

Her ring flew right off her hand while she was gesticulating her story. Her fingers are so fat that I have no idea how this could have happened. She searches for the ring until we get to the old lady's house where she works, then I get out and I help her look.

"It fell down in the seatbelt hole!"

I stick my hand down in there and feel something bite me. I yank my hand out and there's a little blood on it.

"What the fuck? Something bit me!"

"You ever clean this cab, Matt?"

"Maybe it was just a loose spring?" I say, sucking my hand.

"My ring, my ring! You got a wire coat hanger?"

"Shit, Sonja, you got to search the world far and wide to find a wire coat hanger these days."

"Ha, ain't that the truth."

We look for it for ten minutes but have no luck.

"It must be down there somewhere, Sonja, but I have to get going. Was it valuable?"

"Sentimental," she says.

I've never seen her look this sad.

***

The next time I pick her up, that's all she can talk about.

"Did you find my ring, Matt?"

"No, ma'am. I'm sorry."

"Martin's pissed. I have these wind chimes in my room and he was making them jingle all night. He gave me that ring when we was 16 years old. He's pissed I lost it."

"Sic Big Sassy on him," I say.

"Big Sassy's too tired."

***

The next week, it's the same, until about halfway to the old lady's house. Then she starts to scream and jump around in the back seat. I'm on the freeway and the whole cab is shaking and bouncing. Sonja's a big girl, though she has been losing a lot of weight lately.

"What's going on back there?"

"EEK, AHH, it's a bug, you got a BUG back here, Matt! Oh MOTHER OF GOD, I hate bugs! EEEK, THERE IT IS! See it? SEE IT?"

"I'm driving here, Sonja, settle down!"

I get her to the house where she takes care of the old lady and she opens the door before I can stop and kind of jumps/falls out. She's dancing around brushing herself off and shaking her arms. I get out and run around the cab.

"THERE IT IS, THERE IT IS!"

She stomps away mercilessly at the ground for a few minutes and then finally stops and runs about 15 feet away. She's out of breath.

"Is it dead?"

I look at a tiny insect squashed into the gravel.

"Dead as a doorknob."

She comes hesitantly over like she's tiptoeing to the edge of a cliff and looks down, trying to hide behind me even though I'm smaller than she is.

"You got bugs in your cab, Matt."

"Pretty sure you brought that one with you."

"Shit," she says. "I hope that wasn't Martin."

***

The next week, Sonja never calls for her ride. I drive over to her house anyway at around 7:30 in the morning, her regular time. She doesn't answer her phone, so I knock on the door. A tiny old black lady answers.

"Is Sonja going to work today?" I say.

"Sonja isn't here. She ain't coming home no more."

"Where is she?"

"She's with the Lord now, son."

I get back in my cab and sit in her driveway. I'll miss her. I never really believed she lost the ring in my cab; I never saw a ring on her finger. But when I pull out of her driveway, I hear a rattling somewhere under the back seat. It rattles for a week. Every time I turn a corner or apply the brakes, I hear it, back and forth, back and forth...

On Sunday, when I go in to the office to cash out, I put in a request for another cab.

A PAIR TO DRAW TO

It's too early for this shit. The sun is an ember under a bear rug, and I'm full of vinegar. I pull my cab up to the trailer park to find the gates are locked.

I call my fare, which is scheduled for a 4:30 AM pickup. I know the guy. I've taken him to various doctors at least five times; his wife, too. She often tells me the story about a man who broke into her window 15 years ago, beat her near to death, and raped her. She's been on morphine ever since. It's a fucked-up world. Neither one of them ever remembers me.

The phone rings 17 times.

"Yeeeaahhh?" a man says. He's three-quarters asleep.

"Yeeaahhh," I say. "I'm your cab and the gate's locked."

"Oooohh, shit, what time is it?"

"4:26."

"Really?"

"Really."

"Okay, go around to the other gate."

I do it. I'm good at following orders. This gate's locked, too. I call him back.

"This gate is locked too," I say.

"Really?"

"Really."

"Okay," he says, "go back to the first gate. The code is 1234."

27

I go back to the first gate and punch in the uncrackable code, slide into the trailer park, find trailer 36, call him again.

"Yeaaahhh?"

"Ride's here," I say.

"Okay," he says, "we'll be there in a minute."

14 minutes trickle by. The early morning breeze is warm on my cheek from the open window, the creosote breath of the desert.

Finally, he and his wife come out of their trailer. They're both in their fifties. She looks like death on a muffin; he's a sewer-ape in a trench coat. They're both high on morphine and smoking cigarettes. They get in the back. She looks at me.

"What are you, a country music singer?" she says.

I have on a white button-up shirt and jeans.

"No, ma'am, just a cab driver."

"You look like Garth Brooks. Shit, you could pass for Garth Brooks. I mean, except without the voice!"

"Or the money," the man says.

They laugh.

"Where's your boots, Garth?"

"No boots, tennies," I say.

"Well, don't forget to tuck your pants into your boots, Garth!"

The man says, "I can't believe this shit, they're gonna cut me open again, my 12th surgery in five years, but I'm ready. I shaved and even cleaned my ass!"

"We haven't slept all night," the lady says, "I did 16 loads of laundry, made food but didn't eat it. It looked good though, didn't it, honey?

"The dog liked it," he says.

I take the well-paved route to St. Mary's Hospital.

The man says, "The last surgery they cut my throat open and now my tongue is two inches longer. I can touch my nose with my tongue!"

"Honey," the woman says, "that's just because your nose is falling!"

"Oh, yeah," he says.

"We've been playing cards all night," the lady says. "Fucking Susan! Shit! She came over at midnight; she was all greasy and dirty, wasn't she, honey?"

"She said she fell out of a truck," the man says, "ha ha, she won every hand, she won all my Vicodin pills, that bitch!"

"Good people," the woman says.

"Those fucking cops fucked me up," the man says, "they hit me on the back of the neck with their club and now these fucking doctors have to cut me open again! I was on the city bus and got into it with this Mexican, but did the cops hit him? Fuck no! That goddamned bus driver! He was laughing about it! The doctor said if I don't get this surgery, I might be paralyzed. I'm gonna sue those bastard pigs!"

"We'll sue their fucking pig-asses off," the lady says.

There's hardly any traffic. We finally get to the hospital. The giant statue of the Virgin Mary with folded hands stands 30 feet tall at the entrance looking like she's gonna topple face-first into the street. They tumble out of the cab like dice.

"Don't forget to tuck your pants into your boots, Garth!"

"All right," I say.

"Shit," the man says, "we've got time for a smoke!"

I drive away. A few diamonds shimmer over the city like the last hand. Who's winning, who's losing: what a skipping, bouncing, senseless circle. A self-preserving joy grows in fits and starts, depending on the rain. I turn the radio to country and do my math, the numbers like ice. I'm a little ahead, I think, but I can't quit. I have a dream, I have an idea, I have pains inside me no doctor knows about. The streetlights go off one by one as I'm driving beneath them. The sun will come up in a while and roast us all like baby goats; you can bet on it.

GROCERY DAY

Francisca Verdugo needs to go to Food City. I'm a few minutes early, so I sit in my cab and wait for her to come out. The sun shines down on the big, square old folks' building like a penitentiary, the windows sparkling like antique diamonds.

Suddenly from out of one of those first-floor windows jumps a little Chihuahua dog that sprints away like a jail-breaker. An old Mexican lady leans out the window screeches, "Pedro! Pedro!" Then she falls out onto the ground like a sack of beans. She's completely naked, like some wrinkled Latina Eve. She stands up and shuffles after Pedro, but in a couple seconds, she slumps to the ground again.

I get out of the cab and run over to her. She's broken her arm, but is taking it well, smiling. She's drunk, her old naked body hunched there in the hot gravel.

I take off my shirt, but it barely covers her.

"Pedro!" she yells.

"Pedro!" I yell.

Pedro doesn't give a shit.

I dial 911 for an ambulance, lift my nose to the air. Black smoke spirals out her window.

She left a cigarette burning and it caught something. I imagine her dancing around in her lonely room, dreaming about her younger days, pirouetting on her brown, dusty, calloused feet, drinking tequila and smoking cigarettes at age 83, singing forgotten Mexican songs.

31

I call 911 again and tell them to send a fire truck too.

The old lady looks at me, all of her youth gone except for her long black hair and insatiable Indian spirit.

"*Que guapo!*" she says, flirting with me with her shriveled broken arm. Then she looks around again and calls, "Pedro!"

Pedro squats to take a crap next to the only tree around.

The smoke pours out heavy now. Everything must be dried out and ready to burn in there.

I see Francisca Verdugo come out the front doors with her aluminum walker. She looks at me and frowns. I hear the sirens as the old lady clings to me.

"*Ayudame,* good-looking," she says.

When the ambulance gets there, all the men jump out, macho in their uniforms. One of them hustles over and covers her with a blanket. She forgets all about me.

Then the firefighters arrive like storm troopers.

"*Que guapos bomberos!*" she says from her stretcher.

I walk over to Francisca, putting my shirt back on.

"*Lista,* Francisca?" I say. "Ready to go?"

"Who's that?" she says. "Is that Marisol? She's drunk again! *Que borracha,* she's gonna kill us all!"

Smoke barrels up out of the window. Firefighters unroll hoses. Old folks begin to file out with canes and walkers and in wheelchairs.

Francisca and I get in the cab. What are we gonna do: stand around gawking, try to take some lesson from this or draw some meaning? Francisca needs lettuce, chiles, tomatoes, carne, tortillas, I need money, and time's burning up.

As I'm pulling away, I see Pedro zig-zagging through it all, like a streaker on the seventh day of the World Series.

A DAY WITH MELANIE

Melanie's talking as she walks up the sidewalk toward my cab. She's talking as she opens the door. She's talking as I ask her where she wants to go. She'll talk all the way there, and as she gets out and walks away, she'll still be talking.

"...my niece Kathy was born with hair on her back," Melanie says as she gets into the cab, "so maybe that's why she's so crabby all the time. Even at her own wedding. I mean, my God..."

Melanie is a middle-aged nurse. She's short and pudgy, with dark straight hair that is always a mess and falling into her pasty white face. She walks stiffly and always seems about to fall forward. People think she's drunk and sometimes they make comments. Melanie never hears them over the sound of her own voice, which is a blessing.

Melanie hates to drive, so she takes my taxi. She's been in four car accidents and has a bad neck on top of a debilitating fear. She makes good money and sometimes she rents me out for the whole day.

"...at her wedding, Kathy started crying and telling her mother to F-off," she says.

I nod and check the traffic.

"I guess she's just spoiled, you know; everyone always treated her soft because of that hair on her back."

"Did she get it removed?" I say.

"Not yet," Melanie says. "She's 26. Poor girl. Her husband told her that's the first thing they're gonna do: get rid of that hair. Other than that hair, she's a pretty girl."

33

Melanie's cat Tom died a few months ago.

"Are you ready for another cat yet?" I say.

"I don't think so," she says.

I drive her to the Hermitage Cat Shelter on 21st Street. It's a big old house with white tiled flooring and over 400 cats sprawled everywhere, in boxes and cat beds and on cat trees and in cages and on tables and chairs and windowsills and counters and shelves. No rocking chairs. It's a cat lover's paradise. You can just hang out and pet the cats. It's either a cat heaven or a cat hell. This is where Melanie goes to grieve the loss of Tom. At the cat shelter, Melanie knows all the cats' names and greets each one personally.

"Hi, Baxter...oh would you look at wittle Festus...and here comes Duke...how's it going, Dukey? Now where's my Muffin Man?" They come to her asking for attention or stare at her from behind a corner. Sometimes, they try to tell her their sad stories, but they soon find they can't get a word in edgewise, and so they give up and just rub against her legs or sit in her lap and purr.

It's Sunday. After the cat shelter, I take Melanie out to the old mission for Catholic services. It is a 400-year-old Spanish church with a big dome and a courtyard outside of town on a slight rise in the desert. You can see it from miles away and it takes your breath away, even if you know in your heart there is no God and even if you hate what the Spanish did to the natives.

Melanie buys a piece of silver jewelry from an elderly Native American man at the mission. He blesses it and sings a little song to ensure she'll have a good journey in life. Melanie talks to him afterwards. She talks and talks. I slowly lead her away.

When she is in the church, I sit in my cab looking at the desert. A rush runs through me like water and I want to reach out of myself toward the dry red hills. The Native Americans believe the giant saguaro cacti that cover the hills are their ancestors. I look at them standing out there, hundreds of years without a human voice. I'm happy they're like that.

THE HOT LIGHT

My ear sweats with the cell phone pressed against it.

Riiinnnnnggggg. riiinnnnnggggg. riiinnnnnggggg, riiinnnnnggggg, riiinnnnnggggg, riiinnn...

"H-h-hic...hullo?" the woman says.

"Gloria Johnroe?" I say.

"Nooo, she's not here," she says. "Wh—who's calling?"

The woman is crying.

"My name is Matt, I'm the cab driver, here to pick her up."

"Ohhh, owww, sniff, okay," she says. "I'll be right there."

I sit in the cab with the engine running. To turn off the engine would let the 112-degree heat in.

In ten minutes, her apartment door opens and I hear her howling.

"OOOHHHH, MY GAWWWWDDD! OHHH, JEZUSSS, OH, OH, SHIT, OH NOOOO! WOOOH, WOOOH, SHIT, DAMN, OWWWWW, AAHHHH!"

A man's voice comes from her apartment: "SHUT THE HELL UP!"

Then the apartment door slams and she's standing outside alone.

Gloria Johnroe has very large legs. They are elephantine masses of lumpy and cratered meal. She wears small blue shorts and her skin is white and flushed. She slowly swings one leg in front of her, painfully, by her hip, twisting her entire upper torso. She is crying; the whole apartment complex can hear her. She swings, moaning with each glacial step. Her feet

35

have been squished into tiny yellow tennis shoes, like the tied-off ends of a couple of balloons.

When she's at the cab, she rests, leaning against the door and sobbing.

She gets in, which is extremely difficult with her legs the way they are. She stretches her huge legs in front of her, which mash against each other and appear to be one congealed mass. She gets the door latched shut, barely, like closing an overstuffed suitcase from the inside. Or a coffin.

She sniffles a couple of times and catches her breath. I turn the air conditioning up even higher.

A raw, bloody patch of skin shines on her right thigh. She keeps looking at it.

"Burn yourself?"

"Y-y-sort of...my doctor told me I had second-degree burns. I told him, what the hell? I haven't burned myself. And he said I was burning from the INSIDE OUT!"

"I never heard of that," I say.

"Me neither!" Gloria says. "Oooh, it hurts sooo much! I had to take the bandages off this morning and I almost died!"

She sniffles.

"I'm sorry," I say.

I really am sorry, though it doesn't help.

I drive toward Saint Mary's Hospital as safely and efficiently as I know how. I take the curves slowly. We don't talk.

You would think she would just sweat all that out, whatever it is that's making her swell up, especially in a desert summer. But it doesn't work like that. She looks like she's going to explode or melt from the pain. I wonder if she's going to be able to get out of the cab. I think, I'm going to have her with me all day, all week, all year, all my life. The day is too bright, almost blinding, like the Big Bang happened five minutes ago, the hot light going right through everything.

DRANO

It was not possible to pass a kidney stone the size of a golf ball. Cory wouldn't be able to work until after the surgery, which was in a couple of weeks. He needed a break from that taxicab, anyway. He had been driving a taxi ever since he got out of prison twelve years ago, eight years for dealing meth. His old lady rolled on him and she got off scot-free, not a day in jail, even though she did as much dealing and smoking as he did. She never wrote him or visited him when he was inside. When he got out, he tried to contact her. He found her on Facebook, but she wouldn't talk to him and then she blocked him. They had a daughter who was six years old when he got put away. He found her too on Facebook. They talked briefly, once, and she told him it would be best if they didn't communicate. He didn't blame her. She gave him her address and he sent a money order every month. She was now 26 years old and had a new baby of her own. He was a grandfather.

He drove past Randolph Golf Course on his way to Wine and More. The driving range was scattered with a million little white golf balls in the green grass, like stars in the sky. Men and women swung their sticks thinking they were special, fit and tan-legged cartoons. His doctor golfed every other day. The little golf carts puttered and bounced along in a big hurry. Martinis with olives waited in the clubhouse.

At Wine and More, he could hardly walk the aisles. He walked like he had walked that first time in county jail in Los Angeles, years before the prison stint: one foot in front of the other, slowly, head down. One inmate had stepped out of line and the guards jumped on him and beat the shit out of him with their sticks. It was hard to keep track of the timeline. What was it, 34 years ago? He had been only 21. This was before the meth, 1983 or 84.

He had been arrested for multiple driving offenses, marijuana, and coke. He chuckled to think of it now. For years, he had struggled to let it all go, but somehow now he wanted to hold it close to him.

He bought a case of beer and drove slowly back to his apartment. The sun bubbled in the sky like a tick swollen with spoiled butter. How did he ever get to Tucson? Cars and trucks tailgated him and zipped past, only to brake violently and come to hard halts at the red lights and sit there stewing, angry at the universe, though the universe probably didn't do it on purpose. He used to drive like that. Now he realized it made no sense, it did no good. It hurt to brake, it hurt to accelerate. It hurt to breathe.

His apartment was on the third floor and he had trouble climbing the stairs. Inside, he opened a can of beer and sat down to his computer. He popped a pain pill and took a sip of the cold beer. He opened Facebook. Every now and then he posted a photograph of the cosmos, all that space above and around us. There was something calming about the photographs of the galaxy and the stars and the Milky Way, black holes and lazy galactic winds, telescopic photographs that he found on the Internet. Planets. Jupiter was his favorite, with that red storm like a half-developed dragon fetus dropped out of an egg to poach in the churning atmosphere. He posted these photographs on Facebook without any words. What explanation could he give? Nobody ever "liked" his posts or made comments, which didn't bother him. He didn't reach out to anyone, he never trolled. He minded his own business.

In the Los Angeles county jail, the cockroaches were the size of mice. At least he remembered it that way. He was in there for 29 days. Every few days, he was given his street clothes and transported to a different court around the county to be judged and held accountable for the several infractions of which he was accused. Why all of the infractions couldn't have been dealt with in one court on one day was one of those mysteries. None of it made any sense to him. He followed the guards, one foot in front of the other, handcuffed, head down. He was never asked questions. Other people did the talking. The judges sat smug and mighty and fat, sexless ghouls with warty souls. He was always given "time served" and then he was transported back to jail. It was like a game.

In county jail, his cellmate was a kid of 19. The kid had broken into a historical Tucson building and lit a fire and the building had burned to

38

the ground. Before Cory even got snagged, he had seen it on the news, the fire trucks throwing vicious arcs of foaming water into the inferno and the inferno just absorbing it. Later, the ashes and cinders of the building, the brick walls still standing burnt and blackened. The news people made it sound like the "arsonist" was a hardened gangster devoted to the complete destruction of society. And there he was, just a zitty kid laying in the top bunk above Cory, crying. He was awaiting trial and would most likely do 20 years for burning that building. He told Cory he and a buddy had been fooling around, lit a fire in a garbage can for kicks, and then it got out of hand. No sprinkler system in the old building. The kid's buddy had turned him in. Cory celled with this kid for a couple of weeks, heard him jacking off in the night on his bunk, and tried not to look when he shit in the toilet five feet away. Then they took him one morning.

The food in county jail was terrible, but mealtime was still the highlight of the day. In the morning, all they got was bread, cheese, and coffee. In the evenings, they got a little more. On Fridays, they got a hot dog and beans. One Friday, Cory was in line at the food window and the inmate who was standing in front yelled out, "TWO HOT DOGS TODAY!" Everyone in line became excited. But as soon as the screw slid the food tray to the front guy, everyone knew they had been duped. The sadistic cooks had sliced each hot dog longwise and placed them on the trays in such a manner to make it look like two. One inmate laughed and got his ass beat later. Cory laughed to think of it now. There was almost a tenderness in the thought of it.

On his 29th day in county jail, Cory was again given his street clothes and transported to another court to stand before another judge. After it was over, he was led to a door, which he assumed would lead to the white van that would take him back across the county again. The guard took off his handcuffs and opened the door. When Cory walked out, the door shut behind him. He stood there alone behind the court house looking at a freeway ramp. He was free, apparently. But what about his belongings? What about procedure? What the fuck was going on? He walked around the courthouse building to the front door and asked a few people and finally ended up in a clerk's office. The clerk told him his possessions were in the L.A. County Jail and wondered why Cory was so stupid to have left them there.

It took him a day and a half to walk back to L.A. County Jail. When he arrived back at the "glass towers," as they called it back then, he asked around and finally another clerk told him that his belongings were at the original jail of arrest in Newhall, 100 miles away. He had no money, no way to get there. The clerk told him of a thing called "traveler's aid" which he could get at the Greyhound bus station. He slept on the street again and the next day walked into the Greyhound station. He told the ticket lady his story and showed her his jail ID which was all he had. Two hours later, she told him she couldn't get him all the way to Newhall, but she could get him somewhere nearby.

He had not eaten for three days. He slept on the bus. He woke up as the bus was pulling away from his stop. How he knew it was his stop is one of those mysteries, something in his dream told him. He jumped up and yelled at the bus driver, then stumbled down the bus steps into the darkness.

As he walked the dark road to Newhall, a cop stopped him, his campfire top lights swirling in the quiet country night. Cory told him his story and the cop ran his ID and found out he was telling the truth. He gave him a ride into the town jail. He knocked on the jailhouse door, which was locked. Someone came and told him he was lucky because they were about ready to leave. The officer let him in and disappeared for a bit. He returned with a big manila envelope and asked for Cory's ID.

The officer dumped the contents of the envelope on the counter and there it lay: his wallet with a wad of money in it, a bag of pot, a pipe, and a jar of cocaine. His life. The officer asked Cory if these were his. Lowering his head he said yes, sir, they were his. Then, without any other questions, the officer pushed everything over to him and said, okay, there's a bus stop about three miles up the road, good luck. Who can explain these things? No one would believe it, but that's what happened. Outside, he was high within two minutes and it was the best walk of his life.

He hadn't learned a damn thing from all that, and years later, when he was 35, he ended up in the state pen for nearly eight years for selling methamphetamines. After he got out, he stayed out, cleaned up and found a job driving taxi. So many years sitting in that taxi, so many miles, driving, driving, going in circles, going nowhere. He could have driven to Alaska or down to Chile and back again. He could have driven to see his daughter and his granddaughter in Ohio dozens of times. He had no idea where his parents were or if they were alive. When he was 17, his parents went on a vacation to Ireland and never came back. Ireland, of all places! He'd tried for years to find them, and even now he searched for them on Facebook. They could be dead, or maybe they changed their names. They could be any of a million anonymous voices that scratched their pathetic pleas onto the screen.

Somebody knocked on his apartment door. He hobbled over and opened it: it was the girl who lived a couple apartments down in number eight. She stood there fidgety, looking around in a paranoid manner. She was as thin as a corn stalk, except for the pregnant belly. Her fingernails looked like she'd clawed her way out of a worm bucket. She held a coffee cup.

"Hey, dude," she said. "Can I use your microwave?"

"For what?"

"To heat this up."

It wasn't coffee.

"What the fuck is that?"

"Just a little Drano."

"I don't think so. I heat food up in my microwave."

"It's in a cup, man!"

He shut the door. She knocked again. He ignored it. Finally, she screamed, "Bastard!" and stomped away.

Those amateurs were trying to cook meth right in his building. The place might burn down one night. He sat and looked out his front window. He thought of his old cellmate, the kid in county jail who had set fire to the historical building. He should be out of prison by now, if he lived through it. Maybe he could look him up on Facebook? What was his name? For a second, he considered going down to the girl's apartment, helping her. He felt the old, cold urge pulling him. But the pain from the kidney stones kept him from moving. Not even Drano could clean those things out.

Sitting at his computer, he posted a photograph on Facebook, an image of outer space, just a random shot of some stars and a cloudlike cluster, ghostly chaotic, but with a kind of order and beauty. Maybe there was another planet with life on it out there somewhere? He opened the large manila envelope that his doctor had given him, much like the manila envelope that the jail clerk had handed him all those years before. He took out the X-ray and held it up to the window. His kidney stones shimmered, like shrapnel, a few small ones and that big one. His bones, too, Jesus fucking Christ, his skeleton white and porous against the black background. He shuddered. If the stones weren't removed, his body would fill up with poison and he would turn yellow and die. He looked at the picture of the kidney stones and he looked at the picture of outer space taken by the Hubble Telescope. Then he went to his daughter's Facebook page and looked at the photographs of her holding his granddaughter, Muriel. She was a fat little creature, like an alien. He imagined her squirming to escape her mother's belly. He talked to her with his mind, and she understood what he was saying, and she gave him a fragile smile.

The pain diminished a little. He stood up, went outside to the landing of the apartment building. The sun was setting and it lit him up and cooked him. The landing was old and rickety and crooked and slanted down and outward from the apartment building so that you were always being pulled toward the bars of the loose railing. Slowly, he made his way to apartment eight, like a man with a limp, or a lost child walking crosswise on a hill or across the tilted floor of a movie theater. He heard people moving inside the apartment, sharp words, and noticed the familiar chemical smell coming out of the air conditioning unit. He imagined that was what the Earth smelled like when it was young and steaming and toxic and there was no life yet. Either that or the smell of the earth after humankind had burnt it all up. The windows were covered with old newspapers taped around the edges. One of the newspaper pages was the comic page, but it was upside down and Cory couldn't read it.

He was about to knock on the door when he heard the explosion. The landing shook like a small earthquake, or like when you're driving over a bridge with 18-wheelers and wind. The front windows shattered and the glass spit out at him like shards of crystal saliva. The door of the apartment opened and a man stomped out of the smoke, barefoot and bald, a tattooed shirtless devil with an ossified face. He knocked Cory off his feet as he ran off down the landing toward the stairs, which seemed a million miles away. The smoke rushed out inky and billowing and the torn newspapers that had covered the windows curled in filthy orange flames. The girl was still in the apartment with her baby in her belly, but Cory could not get up. His kidney ruptured. He lay on the landing feeling the heat of the fire coming out the apartment door like a pizza oven. He rolled to the railing of the landing and gripped the bars. They were hot and he could feel his fingers melting. For a few seconds, he saw the bald shirtless man running across the parking lot getting smaller. Then all his bones turned soft and he began to slip through the bars like an octopus. The air was like boiling liquid, but it was as if he was born for it and it was salty and thick like blood and the screams he heard were like screams underwater. And then he was through and floating and he had dozens of arms, but he couldn't gather anything into them.

THE CAB KNOWS THE WAY

Whoever Nancy Gantry is, she lives in Bumfuck, Egypt. She's scheduled for a 2:45 PM pickup. My teeth rattle as I progress down the washboard dirt road, like a zipper through the desert. No street signs: just sand, clay, caliche, open range, a few cattle, creosote bush, tumbleweeds, and the massive iodine sun.

I can't find her address. I pull the cab to a dusty stop alongside the road and call Nancy's phone number, which is on the pick-up order. State-paid voucher, $18. Her telephone ring is eardrum-popping rap music. I listen from twelve inches away.

A woman's voice comes on the machine: "Yo, I ain't home, a'hite? Do what you need to do. Peace."

Beeeeep.

I hang up.

Peace, sure. Fuck off.

I keep driving. I finally see an old blue trailer behind a couple of palo verde trees off the road. Two parallel tire tracks parlay through the prickly pears. I follow them in, slowly bouncing my way to the trailer. Junk and garbage cover the ground, beer cans strewn about, some looking at least 40 years old from brands I've never even heard of. Mouse-infested mattresses, rusty box springs, skeletons of cars, broken toys, an old swing set like some medieval torture machine, weight set, heavy bag hanging from the only tree, a gnarled old mesquite, overflowing garbage cans, collapsed swimming pool...

I honk my horn and wait. There is no way I'm getting out of the cab. In a couple minutes, she comes out. She's 75 pounds overweight with a gallon of makeup on her face. Her hair is the color of manure. Her face looks very Irish, very American-Irish.

She gets in the cab.

"How's it going?" she says.

She's as high as a bat. Her movements are herky-jerky, she talks too fast, and she won't look me in the eye. I smell the pot on her, which is undoubtedly mixed with pain pills or meth or both.

"Not bad," he says.

"Any trouble finding the place?"

"Piece of cake."

I start back down the dirt washboard road on the way to Tucson to her doctor.

"Yeah," Nancy says, out of the blue, "I could be a judge."

"Pardon?"

"I was watching *Divorce Court* when you got here," she says. "Not much to do out here."

"I imagine," I say, looking at the bleak, hot landscape. But still, there must be something out there. Mountains in the distance, mountains in the rearview.

"I could be a judge," she says again. "How hard can it be? You should see those people, they're such liars! I can see it in their eyes. I'm great at reading people. I'm great at reading people's eyes."

Nancy turns and looks at me. We both have blue eyes.

I turn onto the highway and kick it up to 75 MPH.

"Shit, I forgot all about this doctor's appointment. I was in my pajamas when you showed up, watching *Divorce Court*. But it's okay; I'm a fast dresser. I've always been a fast dresser. It's the Indian in me."

"Indian?" I say.

"We prefer 'Native American,'" she says.

"You're Native American?"

"1/16th," she says. "I got free health coverage for life. But you should see how they look at me when I go down to the reservation clinic. They look down on me, the other tribe members, you know. They're some prejudiced motherfuckers."

She takes out a bottle of Valium pills and pops one in her mouth.

"Want one?" she says.

"Sure," I say, thinking of later.

"Five bucks," she says.

"Never mind."

"Hey, I gotta make some cash. Freedom Fest is coming up."

"What's that?"

"You don't know what Freedom Fest is?"

"No."

"Dude, are you living under a fucking ROCK?"

She begins to laugh hysterically. She slaps her knees and then slowly calms herself. She peeks around and looks at me again as if she can't believe I'm real.

"Well, I live on the north side," I say.

"Freedom Fest, bro! It's a CONCERT, man, a bunch of bands," Nancy says.

"Gotcha."

"You're fucking with me, aren't you?"

"I wish I was, Mrs. Gantry."

"Dude, you gotta get out once in a while."

"I'm more of a homebody," I say.

"Yeah, well, that's no way to live," she says.

Nancy continues to talk and I respond with a few "hmmms" and "um-humms." I nod. Finally, I don't listen to her at all or give any sign of listening. I go to that place deep inside where I can commit murder without consequence. My face becomes still and relaxed and my neck, too, and my shoulders and arms and hands on the wheel. I don't have to feel anxious or that I am out of place or that anything is wrong. I don't have to pretend that I love what I don't love. I don't have to worry. The cab knows the way.

DODI'S LUCK

Her face has more wrinkles than a crackhead's last dollar bill, but her legs are slim and tight and she has alluring feet with painted toenails like pink little Tums. She has a detonation of naturally blond foliage on her head, unruly enough to camouflage her face. Her hair goes well with her fake boobs, which, 15 years ago, were her 34th birthday present to herself. Dodi once went to the Four Corners up in Utah and she stood in Utah but her boobs were in the other three states.

She sits in her cab in the university area, wondering how she ended up there. I drive up and park next to her. I roll down my window.

"I'm better than this," she says. "What are we doing with our lives, Matt?"

"I don't know, Dodi."

Dodi's been short on cash lately. She's a real human being and she doesn't like getting old. She has a daughter who's in the Navy and she's always bragging about her baby in the Navy. But she hasn't seen her daughter in years.

So many people look sad when you see them sitting in their cars alone at a red light. Dodi's not the only one.

Dodi likes sex, and she figured why not get paid for it? She signed up at an escort agency, Touch of Paradise. The first night, she was sitting in her taxi when her phone rang.

"Susanna?" a woman's voice said. That was her stage name: "Susanna."

"Yes," Dodi—Susanna—said.

"We've got someone for you," the voice said, "over at the Quail."

The Quail was a cheap hotel on Miracle Mile.

"Room 212," the voice said, and hung up.

Dodi went into the bathroom of the Chevron gas station and primped her big blonde hair in the mirror. She looked at herself and didn't like her face. She squirted perfume on her neck and walked back out.

She pulled her taxi into the parking lot of the Quail, which was seedy and getting seedier. A couple of young toughs leaned against the hotel's office door. She found room 212 and walked her high heels up the stairs. She had on a very short blue skirt and a tight, white sleeveless shirt. She always dressed like this, even before deciding to become a part-time hooker.

She knocked on the door and a man opened up. He looked a little nervous. He was not much taller than her, five foot eight with a lean build. He wore blue jeans and a green polo shirt.

"Hi," Dodi said. "I'm Susanna."

"Bill," he said, shaking her hand. "You look great."

"Thanks," Susanna said.

There was a moment of silence as they both stood there looking around. The room was barely disturbed. There was a suitcase on the chair and the bathroom door was open with the light coming out. The place was slightly steamy because of a recent shower. Bill's hair was wet.

"So," Susanna said, "I guess I should ask you if you're a cop."

"Okay," Bill said.

She looked at him and waited.

"Well," she said, "are you a cop?"

"No," Bill said, smiling. "I came to town for the football game, you know, tomorrow night. USC is playing the Wildcats."

"You're from California?" she said.

"L.A."

"I'm moving to L.A. in a year or so," she said.

"The more the merrier," he said.

She sat down on the bed and crossed her legs and waved a foot at him. She dropped her purse gently and seductively to the floor

"It's $200 an hour," she said. "And I need the money up front."

Bill went to the dresser and got his wallet. He walked over and opened it.

"You're under arrest, Susanna," he said, showing her the badge.

They took her downtown and she called June, our boss at the cab company. June went down and bailed her out. She was driving her taxi again the next night.

"I can't do anything right," Dodi said to me while we sat there in our cabs.

A good-looking college girl walked by, laughing into her cellphone. She walked in front of Dodi's cab and Dodi gave the horn a quick punch. The college girl jumped and dropped her cellphone. She scowled at Dodi, bent down, picked up the phone, and hurried away. Dodi and I laughed for a bit, and I lit a cigarette. Then we were quiet and sat there waiting for fares.

THE THING PEOPLE DON'T UNDERSTAND

She comes into my apartment from the heat of the desert day.

"Hi, Mary," I say.

"Hi, Matt," she says.

She stands in the middle of the room and fans herself with her small hand.

"Whew," she says. "That cab was hot. And I don't think the driver had bathed in a week!"

Her face is flushed and she smiles. Then she starts taking off her clothes. It's a small apartment that is one big room. I am sitting at my kitchen table next to the fan.

"How is everything?" I say.

"My love life's gone to hell," she says. She looks at the ceiling while she takes off a sock standing on one foot.

"Problems with Ernesto?" I say. I stand up from the kitchen table and sit down on the bed. I have on a pair of shorts and a T-shirt.

"He's so closed off," she says. She folds her clothes and places them on a chair. "He never lets anyone inside." She points to her heart. "He told me that he has never been in love in his entire life. 50 years old and he's never been in love."

She comes over and stands there naked. She's 49 years old. Her belly and legs are like melting candles. Her breasts are small and still nice and her face is youthful and pretty.

She sits down next to me and starts absentmindedly stroking my penis

53

through my shorts. I take off my shirt.

"It's not easy to find someone you like," I say. "And then it never lasts."

"You're telling me," she says. "What are you? 41? 42?"

I nod.

"Just wait," she says. "You'll find out how hard it is. Every man my age looks like a grandpa. And I don't care what they say: sex appeal is important."

"I've seen a few 50-year-old men who look pretty good," I say.

"Sure," she says, "and do you know what? They are so arrogant."

"Did you ever have sex with Ernesto?" I ask.

"No," she says. "But I wanted to." She lets out a gasp. "He has the biggest thighs I've ever seen."

She squeezes one of my skinny thighs while she says this.

"Then what's the problem?"

"Well," she says, "Ernesto is old fashioned. I knew he wouldn't respect me if I slept with him right away."

"How long have you dated?"

"Six months."

"You're a tease."

"Well," she says, "I know he has women he sleeps with, you know, just casual sex."

"Then why's he dating you?"

"Because he's looking for something better, something real, something emotional. There is a difference, you know, between sex that is emotional and sex that is just casual sex."

"I know."

"It's sad," Mary says. "He's such a smart man. I don't want to sound vain, but it's rare I meet a man who is smarter than me."

"Did he know about your, uh, side hobby?"

"Oh, no, I wouldn't tell him."

"So you'd just quit doing this if you get serious with him?" I say.

"Probably."

"You'd just quit cold turkey?"

She pats my stomach. "Don't worry," she says, "I'd give my regulars plenty of warning. Besides, it's not going to happen." She reaches down into her purse and gets out a condom. "The other day, I told Ernesto we should just be friends."

"Thank God."

"I gave him plenty of time," she says, "and my mother liked him. She liked him a lot, and he liked my mother, too, which is important."

"Very."

"I mean," Mary says, "I trust my mother. I really trust her. Almost everybody knows their mother loves them, but not everybody feels it."

"I think you're right," I say.

"I feel it," she says, "I really feel it. My mother has always loved me. She's always shown me and told me how much she loves me."

"I haven't seen my mother in a while."

"You should call your mother."

"I know."

"But," she says, "me and my mother agree that there is something about Ernesto that won't let him get close to anybody. I'm not a young woman anymore. I want someone to settle down with, someone who can love me and let himself be loved. It's very hard for some men to let themselves be loved."

She pushes me back and takes off my shorts and puts a condom on me and puts me in her mouth. She straddles my left leg and her small breasts brush against the hair on my thighs. I look down at her shoulders, which are a little rounded and coarsened with a few freckles, but still nice. I run my fingers through her hair. Her hair is rough and dyed brown. I reach down and stroke her ass. My fingers get a little too close to her asshole and she gives me an "oh, no, you don't" sound like a mother catching a child trying to dip his fingers into the icing bowl. I go back to her hair.

She stops sucking and looks up at me. "You know what really did it?"

she says. "He invited me and mother to his house for dinner. It was the first time I'd ever been in his house. Anyway, his house was very...very, tidy."

"Too tidy?"

"It was like it wasn't lived in, like no one really lived there. Mother felt it, too, and we talked about it all the way home. There was just something wrong with the whole scene."

"I'm sorry, Mary."

Afterwards, she gets dressed. I lay back on the pillow still naked.

"How about you?" she asks, "Dating anybody yet?"

"No. No time."

"Well," she says, "us girls do need a little time."

"Among other things."

"The thing people don't understand," she says, "is men and women are different, very fundamentally different. It's amazing to me we can get along at all."

She walks over to my desk and picks up the five $20 bills I had placed there. Then her pager goes off. She looks at it and then looks at me and smiles.

"Bye, Mary," I say.

"Bye, sweetie."

Her cab pulls up outside. She had told the driver to come back in an hour. She walks out into the sun, leaving the door open like she always does. I stand up and walk over and reach out for the doorknob. I stand there for a few seconds, squinting into the glare.

DON'T DIE BEFORE YOUR MOTHER

Outside the hotel, two little old ladies climbed into the back seat of my cab and felt the air conditioner.

"2212 North Inn Road," one of them said.

"Are you sure it's not North INA Road?" I said into the rearview mirror. I had long, scraggly brown hair and my eyes looked as red as a sunset.

"No, no, no," the same woman said. "2212 North Inn Road. I should know my own son's address, shouldn't I?"

The other woman was silent.

"2212 North Inn Road is a bowling alley," I said.

"No, it's not, it's my son's house," she said. "What's your name, sir?"

"Matt."

"Well, *Matt*," she said, "when we get there, you'll see."

So, I drove over there and we sat looking at the bowling alley.

"What else can happen, Linda?" she said. "We came all the way from Chicago, we put an ad in the paper that cost me $140, and now the cab driver doesn't know where John's house is."

"Ma'am," I said, "you have the wrong address."

She exploded. "I DON'T HAVE THE WRONG ADDRESS! JESUS! What's going on? First my son goes and croaks on me, and now I've got to deal with all this."

Linda nodded and kept her fat hands in her fat lap. I called my boss over the two-way radio.

"They've got the address wrong," my boss, Harriet, blurted over the crackle. "She must be talking about North *Ina.*"

"You tell that lady she is in the wrong business," the old woman said, pointing her wrinkled old finger at the radio.

"She's been driving a cab in this town for 30 years," I said.

"Look," she said, "my son is dead. I have to find his house and sell it. Okay?"

"I'm sorry."

"Do your mother a favor," she said. "Get a wife. Get a wife so your mother doesn't have to deal with it when you croak. You married?"

"Yes," I said.

"Good boy," she said.

"John ate fast food every day," the woman said. "He was a bachelor. He moved here when he was 19, and that's just what bachelors do: they eat fast food and don't worry about it."

"Can't you call someone about the address?" I said.

"I don't have a phone," she said. "Do you think everyone in the world has a cell phone?"

I handed her my cell phone.

"Who am I going to call?" she said.

"You could call Geneva," Linda said quietly.

"I guess I could call Geneva," Diane said.

She managed to dial the number in three attempts.

"Be there, Geneva," Diane said, while it rang. "For once in your life, be there—hello, Geneva, it's Diane..." She sighed as she realized it was only an answering machine.

Frustrated, I pulled back onto the road and headed back toward their hotel.

Well, then she sure got busy with that phone. She kept calling numbers, but no one answered.

"Isn't anyone home?" she said.

She finally got a busy signal. She waited a minute and then called the number again. It rang, and rang, kept ringing.

"It was busy a minute ago," Diane said.

"Some vacation," Linda said, looking out the window at the brilliant day. Three blocks from their hotel, at River and Campbell, by miracle, a human being was contacted on the phone. However, Diane couldn't seem to get the person on the other line to understand the situation. So she handed the phone to me.

"Hello?" I said.

The other person on the line turned out to be a 93-year-old woman in Summum, Ohio.

"Do you know where we are going?" I said loudly.

"Yes," the old woman on the phone said.

"How do we get there?" I said.

"Where are you now?" the old woman said.

"On River Road."

"That's not where it is," the old woman said.

"You don't say," I said.

"It's a long way from there," the old woman said.

"What's the closest cross street?"

"It's off of Park Avenue..."

I hung up.

"Well?" Diane said accusingly. "You figure it out?"

"It's on North INA, which is off Park," I said.

Diane sank back in her seat and braced herself for the G-forces of my U-turn. Linda had a slight smile on her face.

When I pulled up to 2212 North Ina, she said, "There it is, I told you!" The meter said $74.45. I only charged them $50 because I felt sorry for them.

Diane told me they needed a ride back to the hotel at four that afternoon. They were not going to sleep in a dead man's house. It would be another $50, so I agreed.

When I showed up at four to take them back to the hotel, they were standing in the yard behind the closed security gate. It was heavy steel, about six feet tall. When I had dropped them off earlier, the gate was open. The rest of the property was surrounded by a cement block wall.

I wondered about the strange son who had died before his mother. I pulled up and got out of my cab and looked at them standing in there like captured animals, half-blind in the afternoon sun. Diane had white, short-cropped hair. She reminded me of an effeminate man. Linda was Hispanic. She had dark skin with hundreds of little brown moles all over the sides of her face and neck. She used a cane because of a bad right hip.

"Damn thing shut on us, it's fucking haunted!" Diane said, holding the bars like someone in jail. "Can you believe this?"

She asked me for my phone and she started dialing numbers.

"I can't wait here all day," I said.

"Go on, go on," Diane shooed me away. "We'll call the fire department and they'll come and get us out of here."

I stood there. Shit.

I climbed over the fence with some difficulty.

"There must be a switch or something," I said, out of breath.

We looked everywhere, inside and outside the house; no switches.

I saw a ladder in the backyard of the neighbor's house, climbed back over the wall, and knocked on the door. No one answered, so I went around back and grabbed the ladder anyway.

"How's Linda going to climb a ladder?" Diane said.

"We could try," I said. Linda gave a small nod of consent.

I leaned the ladder against the wall and held it.

"Okay, Linda," I said.

She hesitantly stepped up to the ladder.

"I've got you," I said, holding the ladder while Linda slowly lifted her left foot up to the first rung. She reached the second rung and then the

60

third, one at a time, each a great effort. If she toppled backwards with her weight, there wouldn't be anything I could do about it.

At the top, she celebrated with a "Hurrah!" Then she realized she could not lift her leg up over the wall.

"Try going up backwards," I said.

The slow process began again downwards and then she turned around and started to put her foot up backwards.

"Like this?" she said.

"You can do it."

She did it. At the top, she moved, one inch at a time, her fat ass onto the wide flat top of the cement block wall. I put my hand on the pendulous waddle of her upper arm. She got both her legs over and was sitting on the wall with me and was quite happy about her accomplishment. She giggled. I moved the ladder over the fence and hopped over and situated the ladder under Linda from the other side.

"Okay," I said. "Come on down." She began to lower herself and we held our breath.

All this time, Diane was talking on my cell phone.

"Yes, Jackie," Diane was saying, "we tried that. We've tried everything. No, I can't get hold of Bill. I can't get hold of Bill and the cab driver's here and it already cost me $73 for the cab ride, and he couldn't find the address and then we stayed out here all afternoon and no buyers showed up..."

I noted what she said about the fare being $73 instead of the $50.

"...they got a ladder," Diane said, "What?...Yes, Linda's going over right now."

Diane smiled at Linda, who was just then reaching the ground on the other side.

"Land," Linda said, like a sailor after months at sea.

"...okay," Diane said. "Bye."

Diane handed the phone up to me. "My daughter," she said. "She lives in Michigan. I thought she might know something. But of course, she didn't. Watch: she'll die on me next."

61

She nimbly climbed up the ladder and over the wall, a regular gymnast.

"Some vacation," Linda said.

"But you climbed the ladder," I said.

"I can't believe I did it," she beamed. "What was I thinking?"

"Let's get the hell out of here," Diane said. "If John was here, I'd kick his ass, I swear I would."

We all climbed into the cab and were laughing by the time we were halfway back.

I showed Diane and Linda a bakery near their hotel and suggested they have breakfast there. I rolled up to the hotel doors. Diane paid, including a tiny tip. They moaned and groaned with the creaking of old bones as they climbed out of the cab and stood on the sidewalk. They waved goodbye and disappeared into the resort lobby.

"232 Clear," I said into the radio mike.

"10-4, 232," the dispatcher said.

I sat there for a minute. Then I slowly drove over to Jacob's Park. I dialed a number on my cell phone, back in Illinois, but then didn't make the call.

BOB'S BIG DAY

It's like two in the afternoon and the computer screen spits a fare at me from zone 577. 4500 North Oracle, the mall. I pull my cab up to the Cheesecake Factory entrance and there's this guy sitting on the sidewalk next to a couple of mall cops. Great, just what I fucking need.

I get out of the cab, and one of the mall cops says: "Okay, here's the deal: this guy is WASTED."

"Wonderful," I say.

"But," the mall cop says, "he's got a big wad of cash."

Okay, I think, *that's a little better.*

We get the drunk guy in my cab, I mean he's fucking gonzo, has no idea where he is, hasn't said a word yet. Some middle-aged dude.

"Hey, buddy," I say. No response. "Hey, BUDDY! Where you wanna go?"

He comes out of his trance and says, "Daze Inn." The Days Inn, you know, down by the freeway there. The easiest way to get there is to take a left on Oracle and head down. So I go out and take a right on Oracle, head north.

"How ya doing, man?" I say.

"Uh neeed sum FUCKIN BEEEER," the guy says.

"Beer, huh? No problem, I'm your man, I got your back."

So I drive a mile or two up Oracle, passing a few stores, then finally pull into a Circle K.

"What you need, partner?" I ask him.

"Gimme an 18-pack of BUD!" the guy says.

He fishes into his pocket and pulls out this big wad of money, gives me two twenties. I go in, stroll around for a while, then buy a six-pack of Bud for five bucks. I go back out to the cab.

"Fuck this store," I tell him, giving him the beer but not the change. "All they had was six packs!"

He just grunts and I get driving again. I take a left on Limberlost and head that way. He falls asleep back there in the cab and I drive around for a while.

Then I say, "Hey, BUDDY! How ya doing?"

He wakes up and grunts, "Uh need some BEEEER."

"Some beer it is!" I say. "Let's get some beer."

So I take a right on Stone and go up there for a bit. Then I pull into a Circle K.

"What you want, man?"

"Gimme an 18-pack of BUD!"

"Alright, but I need some cash."

He fishes out two more twenties and I go in and come back out, tossing him a six-pack.

"What the fuck?" I say. "This store only sells six-packs!"

"Fucking Tucson," the guy says, "Fuck this town!"

"Fucking Mormons!" I say. He agrees.

So I start to head east on Roger Road.

In a few miles, he grunts, "Hey, uh need some BEEEER! I gotta have 18 beeeers!"

So...I pull into ANOTHER Circle K, but when I pull in there, he says, "I need something ta eat too! I need a hot dog!"

"Well," I say, "You know, QuikTrip has the best hot dogs in town."

"Less go!"

So I pull out of the Circle K and head north on Campbell. I pass a couple of Quick Trips and finally pull into one.

"I'm gonna need some cash, man."

Another couple of twenties.

"Don't forget the beer!"

"Not a chance! And a hot dog, too, right?"

"You're arrright, man," he says.

I go in and get him a six-pack of Bud and a hot dog. Seven bucks. I put the change with the rest of it in my pocket. I go back out. By this time, he's got his 18 beers and he's happy with that hot dog. I figure I'll just take him to the hotel.

When we get to the hotel 20 minutes later, I say, "Hey, man, what you gonna do? I mean, shit, it's only three o'clock in the afternoon."

"Shiiit, ain' nothin' ta do in this fuck-ass town."

"How about a strip club? You want to see some titties?"

He likes this idea.

"Yeah! Lemme jes put this beer in the room and I'll be r'back."

"Okay," I say. "But I need to settle this meter first."

The meter says $42.

"How much issit?"

"$50. Plus a tip for all the beer running I did."

He gives me three more twenties and I pocket them.

Then he gets out and stumbles to the door with one of the six-packs because that's all he can carry. I take the other two six-packs and hide them under my coat in the front. He can't get the key in for shit and leans his head against the hotel room door. Then he drops the six-pack, and when he tries to bend over to pick it up, he does a face plant on the sidewalk. I get out to help him and we get the door open. I'm standing there with the six-pack in my hand and he goes inside and collapses on the bed. *Well*, I think, *that's all she wrote.*

"Okay, buddy," I say. "It looks like the strip club is off."

"Ohhmmmmffffuckemffff."

"Hey! Hey, BUDDY! I'll leave you be, but I got to be paid for the meter."

"The whaaat?"

"The meter, man, you took a cab ride and you gotta pay the meter. I gotta get paid for the ride."

"Whaddya think I'm STOOOPID?!"

"Come on, man, don't be that way, I got a kid to feed, I'm just trying to make a living."

He gets up off the bed and stands there wobbling in the room.

"Look, I got you this beer. But if you don't want to pay me, then I'll just take it."

I take the beer and go back outside and get in the cab, lock the doors. He comes out and stands by my window.

"Hey, isss cool, man, give me the beer."

"40 bucks," I say, pointing at the meter.

He brings out his wad and gives me two more twenties.

"Okay," I say, then get out and hand him the beer.

"Where's the ress ovit?" he says.

"That's all, man, that's all you bought."

He looks into the back seat and so do I and that's when I see the back seat is filthy from his hot dog. I mean there's fucking bits of hot dog and catsup and shit all over the place. I open the back door and show him.

"Shit, look at the seat! I'm gonna have to get that cleaned! Give me another 20 bucks for the car wash!"

"God dammmmit!" he screams. "I FUCKIN' HATE THIS TOWN!" He does a little drunk fit there in the parking lot of the Days Inn, kind of dancing around, throwing his arms up in the air.

"Just be cool, man, the car wash is gonna charge me 20 bucks to get that cleaned, and if I take the car in like that, they'll fire me!"

He gives me another twenty.

"Shit," he says and stumbles back to his room with his six-pack.

66

As I'm pulling out, I see a bunch of Mexicans working on one of the hotel rooms. They're painting it or something.

"Hey guys!" I say. "You want some beer?"

Claro, they want some beer.

I show them the twelve Buds. "Five bucks," I say.

One of them gives me a five. Then I'm out of there.

This ain't really a bad town, you know, if you give it a chance.

NOTHING BUT A HUMAN BEING

It was 5AM, dark, and there was a steak knife in the road. I drove right over it in my cab, heard a clink and zing fade into the darkness.

Amy Dunne sat in the passenger seat. I was taking her to her kidney dialysis, like every Monday, Wednesday, and Friday for the last two years. Amy was wild haired and prickly as always. When your kidneys go bad, you can't take liquids. I tried to imagine living in the desert and not being able to drink a glass of water.

"What was that noise?" Amy said.

"I didn't hear anything," I said.

"Don't screw with me!"

"Must be in your head, Amy."

"Hmmmmph."

Like many people with physical problems, Amy had mental problems, too. The two kinds of problems seemed to go hand in hand, and I didn't know where the line was.

At the dialysis center, I got out of the cab to get Amy's walker from the back and then I heard it: the hiss of air streaming out the back rear tire. I looked down and saw the steak knife blade sticking out of the tire, the handle broken off. It was as if someone had done it on purpose.

Amy went into the dialysis center and I drove very slowly over to a quieter and more level part of the parking lot. I found the car jack and lug nut wrench in the trunk. I got the small spare donut tire out. The only light was from the streetlamp. I had never had a flat tire while driving this particular vehicle; it was new to me, the company had dozens of these cabs. I put the emergency brake on and tried to figure out how to use the jack. Every car jack in the world was as unique as a fucking snowflake.

I got the car jacked up and felt the strain in my forearms and back and neck. I was 42, looked 50, with gray hair and a belly. I was weak and dizzy with something that seemed to roll over like a sleeping animal in my right ear. The areas around my eyes were dark and heavy as motor oil. I was sweating. It was 85 degrees, even though the sun was not up yet.

I got the tire off and put the spare donut on, then lowered the car. I threw the jack and wrench in the trunk. My shirt was filthy, but there was no time to get cleaned up. I spit on my hands and found some paper towels in the glove box. I drove to my next pickup, which was at six o'clock in the morning: Jen Trujillo, 1246 East Fort Lowell, apartment number 2. Phone number: 520-985-1665.

I arrived at 5:55 and phoned her.

"Hullo?"

"Your ride's here, Mrs. Trujillo."

"Already?" she screeched. "You're not supposed to be here until six!"

"Forgive me," I said.

Jen was 54, a chronic pain patient, a doctor-hopper and pill-chaser. She received monthly government checks for some indefinable but insurmountable inability to work.

Jen trudged her fat ass out of her apartment in her bedroom slippers and pink bathrobe over blue jeans. She held an insulated soda mug as big as a pony keg and cradled it in her lap when she got in the cab.

At the four-way stop by her apartment, a huge black truck flew right through it and would have hit us if I hadn't slammed on the brakes.

"God fucking damn," she said. "Take it easy."

"I forgot to take my valium," I said.

"Can I smoke?" she said.

"No."

"I hate these early appointments," she said. "This quack better write me a script."

70

"The unbearable pain?" I said.

"Oh, dude, you don't even know," Jen said. "I'm in so much pain. When I talk on the phone, my hand goes numb. Shit, it's gonna be a long fucking day."

Her idea of a long day was getting herself out of bed, popping a couple of Percocets, assembling a gigantic soda, smoking cigarettes which she sold food stamps to buy, getting chauffeured to a doctor, getting looked at by a doctor, and getting chauffeured home again.

"You'll plow through," I said.

When Jen went into her doctor's, I had 20 minutes to take a break. I went into the doctor's building and found a bathroom, where I cleaned myself up. Then I went back and sat in the cab. I watched some Mexican guys at a construction site across the street. They were building a brick wall with oversized bricks. One guy stooped down and picked up a brick from the stack. He tossed it about five feet to another guy who caught it, then turned and tossed it another five feet to another guy. The last guy slapped it onto the progressing wall, slathered it with a cement mixture with his big, flat knife, cleaned it off like a teppanyaki chef, and turned to wait for another brick.

I looked at my hands. I was softer than puppy shit. Those bricklayers weren't even wearing gloves. And they would do it all day, even later, when it was 110 degrees. Sometimes, my dick went numb from sitting in the cab so long, and I had to dig my hand into my pants and stretch it out until it regained life.

My seven o'clock pick-up, Mattias Olsen, 401 South Park, didn't answer his phone. *Okay, Mattias,* I said to myself, *you fucking asshole.*

I climbed out of the cab like it was the hardest thing I'd ever done. I went to the door of the apartment and pressed the bell. In a minute, the door opened an inch.

"Yeah?" a man's voice said.

"Ride's here," I said, and turned and walked away.

"Oh, shit," the guy said. "I'll be right there."

Oh, shit, right, I said to myself. *Oh, shit! Can't even keep his doctor's appointments straight, can't even get himself ready to go. Yeah, he says. Yeah?*

71

What do you think, jackass? Your fucking FREE RIDE is here! Yeah?

I got back into the cab, still mumbling. I waited another five minutes. I was ready to kill Sir Mattias when he finally opened the door and came out.

Mattias was about 30, and he had a cane. He walked very slowly and looked straight ahead. He walked like he was 100 years old.

"Sorry I made you wait," he said when he got in beside me.

"S'okay."

"No," he said, "it's not okay. I'm almost always ready, but today, well, it's been a rough morning."

"Tell me about it."

"They put the wrong pin in my leg," he said. "I've got this metal pin that goes from my knee to my foot, and the surgeon put the wrong one in there."

"Hmmm."

"So it's hard to move too fast. They've got to take out the pin and put in another one. The first time they almost had to cut my leg off, and this time they don't know what will happen, but they've got to get that pin out of there."

"Hurts, huh?"

"You could say that," he said. "Some old guy T-boned me. He was 87 and blind in one eye. He just didn't feel like giving up his license and he didn't feel like stopping at that red light."

"The cops got him?"

"They didn't do shit to him. He was some rich fuck, I didn't get squat out of the deal. Fucking lawyers."

"Unbelievable."

"I had some brain trauma, too. Do you know how many pills I take a day?"

"10?"

"32!"

"Where'd the accident happen?" I said.

"Craycroft and 22nd."

I knew it intimately.

I dropped Mattias off at a doctor's office over near St. Joseph's Hospital. Mattias waved and limped away into the oblivion of the medical system.

After that, I went down to the mechanic shop and had a new tire put on. I didn't know what to do while I waited. I was having hot and cold spells, my face was flushed like I was going to have a stroke, and my hands and neck trembled. I hadn't been to the doctor in 15 years, had no insurance, no spare money. I stood in the hot sun outside the auto garage.

I wandered around the auto yard, towards the back. It was a quarter acre packed with wrecked vehicles, a boneyard. I read on the sides of dozens of them: NICE AND EASY TRANSPORTATION. My cab had the same sign. It was so easy to get hit by another vehicle on the street, or to lose your concentration for a second, the wrong second. Just like that, poof, everything could change. I almost hit a little girl the other day. She was running across the street chasing a ball. I knew how easy it was to slip, going 80 MPH with only inches between me and several hundred other cars on the freeway, and I knew that behind the tinted glass there was a human being at the wheel, nothing but a human being, pretending to be in control.

I looked at those wrecked cars and felt my face.

"Sir!" a voice came from inside the garage. "Sir!"

I looked and a young mechanic was waving at me. I nodded. The tire was fixed, the cab was ready. Great. What were you going to do? I walked over and thanked the kid. I got in the cab, started it up. I had a 12 o'clock pick-up: Virl Green, 123 W. Jacinto. Virl was an annoying little prick who thought the world owed him something.

JOHN'S DREAM

John leans to one side when he walks, always ready to fall, and he has a hard time keeping his eyes open. For years, he was homeless, sleeping in the Rillito Wash, until some stranger finally helped him get into a state facility apartment where they make sure he takes his medication every day. He's 56 years old, very skinny with a bad complexion and brown, crooked teeth. He's never had a girlfriend or even considered that a possibility.

As a condition of living in the state facility, John has been given a job and a free cab ride to work. I pick him up three times a week in my cab. He works at a place where they employ people with disabilities, autistic people, Down syndrome, and others with hard-to-categorize problems. The building where he works is a big metal warehouse. The many hundreds of people who work there sit at long metal tables on hard metal chairs and do menial tasks, such as sorting bolts and nuts into boxes, or screwing simple screws into the proper holes on small machinery parts, or separating molded-plastic pieces to be ready for sale in stores. Some of the workers on the assembly lines are crippled, some of them can't talk, some scream and moan and cry, some drool or go to the bathroom on themselves. Their ages vary from 18 to 60. At lunchtime, there is a lunch counter where they can eat if they do not bring their lunch. The cost of the food comes out of their paychecks, which amount to about $25 a week. Some of them need to be fed like children, but most can feed themselves. John likes his job and never complains about it. In fact, I've never heard him complain about anything.

But John's life doesn't revolve around his job. His passion is writing. He's a writer, and very proud of being a writer. John writes a story—sometimes two stories—every day, and he has done this for years and years.

75

His stories are just a page or two. Quick and to the point is how he puts it. But with a twist, he says. That's very important. When I take John to work, he always tells me about the story he wrote the day before. Sometimes, he has a hard time coming up with an idea for a new story, having written so many, and he asks me to help him. Anything can be a story, he says; just give me an idea. I drive along the streets of Tucson on the way to the warehouse and I say something like, well, how about that antique store, John, you could write a story about an antique store. And he says, you've got a good one there, I could write a story about an antique store. He thinks about it for a minute, then he says: maybe there's an employee at the antique store who sees an antique picture and is transported into the picture and lives there for a while. Or I'll see a car wash and I'll say: you could write a story about a car wash, John. And he'll think about it and say: maybe there is a guy who takes his car into the car wash and when he's in the car wash he is transported to another dimension. John can write about anything.

John doesn't like the food that they make at the warehouse or at his state facility, so he eats at Whataburger, which is next door to where he lives. He's allowed to walk that far, and no farther, on his own. He eats there when he gets home from work, always the same thing: a regular hamburger, small fries, and a Coke for five dollars and 35 cents. Sometimes, there's a nice girl working there who will give him a free refill on the Coke, but most times it's just the one. He always runs out of money before his next paycheck and then he can't eat at Whataburger for a few days. On those days, he is forced to eat whatever is served to him.

One time, John was struck by a car while walking across the street to Whataburger. His already bad leg was made even worse, and three years later, he was finally given a settlement of $500 for his pain and suffering. As I am his cab driver and possibly his best friend, he offers to treat me to lunch at Whataburger with part of his settlement. On my day off, I go to Whataburger at 11 o'clock to have lunch with him. Get whatever you want, he says, though I recommend the hamburgers. I order a hamburger and we sit at a table in the sun and eat.

What did you write yesterday, John? I ask him.

I wrote a story about this guy who works in a warehouse, he says. This guy doesn't have anybody in the world and he works at this warehouse and the work isn't very much fun and he doesn't like it very much, but he's happy enough. The warehouse doesn't have any windows and is kind of cold and the light is too bright, but it's not too bad. There is also a lunch counter where the employees eat, but the guy never likes the food. He eats it or sometimes he doesn't eat it. Then, one day the guy dies, right there on the assembly line, and he goes to Heaven. When he is in Heaven, he discovers Heaven is like a big warehouse with metal walls and much the same as where he was before. No windows, but not too bad. He thinks it is exactly the same. But when he goes to the lunch counter, he finds they have much better food. Instead of eggs, there is lobster. Instead of fish sticks, now there are hamburgers.

That's a good one, John, I say.

Eat up, he says, It's on me.

One day, I go to pick John up and he isn't there. A lady comes out and tells me they can't find him; he must have wandered off somewhere. A week later, he's still missing. The lady tells me they've given up. I ask to see his room and she's nice enough to let me in. The room is filthy and stinks. They're gonna clean it out tomorrow, the lady tells me. Notebook papers lay scattered everywhere, on the floor, on the little table, on the bed, in the bathroom. The notebook papers are covered with illegible pencil scribbles, partial sentences and misspelled words or just messy lines. I pick one up. It is complete nonsense.

When John got his settlement of $500 for getting hit by a car, he wanted to use some of the money to buy a computer to put all his stories in. The place where he lived gave a group of residents a ride in their big white van to the Tucson mall one Sunday. The van dropped the group off at the mall and the driver told them they would have two hours at the mall, after which they would be expected to be back at that same spot for the return trip. John was so worried about missing the ride home that he just walked into the mall and turned right around and walked back out and sat on the bench and waited to go home. He sat on the bench and thought about the next story he would write: maybe it would be about a guy sitting on a bench outside a mall watching a little ant crawl over his shoe, and maybe the guy would talk to the ant, and the ant would talk back, and the ant would tell him things. John's dream was to have a book published of all his stories.

I look for John when I'm driving the streets in my cab. I even took a long walk along the Rillito Wash one weekend. No sign of him. I guess it would be fitting to go to Whataburger and eat a hamburger in his honor once a month, write a story in a sunny booth with a pencil on a notepad, a story about anything that comes to mind, a story quick and to the point, with a twist. But I don't. The food at Whataburger is not very good, and I don't have the imagination for it.

GOD DIDN'T GET ME NO WEED

Me and Little John were sitting at the Greyhound bus station behind the wheels of our taxicabs. We were toward the end of the cab queue and wouldn't get a fare for a while. It was a depressing place to be, number nine or ten in the bus station cab queue at four in the afternoon. It was hotter than a whore on dollar day.

Little John was on his cell phone. His seven teeth flashed in the sun.

"Hey, Donny," he said into the phone. "What's up? Where you been?"

He looked at me through our open windows and gave me the thumbs up.

"What?" he said. "No, no, man...hey, is Jay there?...Where is he?... Don't fuck around man, I'm completely out, I mean, I had a couple of buds stashed away for an emergency, but those are gone now and...What?...No, hey, you know me, man, I can't live like this. I AM A MAN WHO NEEDS HIS WEED! Ray? Ray? Hello?"

Little John looked at me again. "Fucker hung up," he said. "He's blowing me off, man. But I'll get to him if I have to drive this fucking taxi all the way to fucking Yuma."

Little John was five foot six and weighed 245 pounds. He had bad arches that caused him to walk with a stiff-legged lurch, but he hardly ever walked; he mostly remained behind the wheel of his cab. He was most comfortable there and had the appearance of being a physical part of the vehicle. He was 44 years old with over-washed salt-and-pepper hair that fell down his neck and onto his Neolithic forehead. A wart poked, nipple-like, out of his right cheek, and he rubbed it while he talked.

"Don't smoke pot before you come to work," the boss told Little John one time.

"Be reasonable," Little John said.

"Well, don't smoke at least three hours before work."

"One hour."

"Two and a half."

They settled on two hours, but Little John smoked throughout his whole shift anyway. He smoked everywhere, many times right in his taxi.

Today, he ran out of weed for the first time in years.

"I can't live like this," he said to me. "I've got to work, I've got to drive this fucking taxi, I've got to make money. I've got to deal with these people, all these motherfuckers..."

"Easy," I said. "God is listening."

"Fuck God," Little John said. "God didn't get me no weed. You hear me, motherfucker?" He leaned his head out his cab window and looked at the sky, where God lived. He shielded his eyes from the sun and yelled, "Fuck YOU!"

He brought his head back inside the cab, looked straight ahead, and sighed. He sat there for a second. Then he gave me a worried look and put his head back out the window.

"Just kidding," he said to the sky.

A white van pulled into the bus station parking lot. A fat corrections officer got out and opened the door, and four men hopped out wearing their blue jail shirts. This is standard procedure for released convicts who have no one to come pick them up. Whether the convicts have money for a bus ticket or where they go from there is of no concern to the corrections officers. They just drive away.

Val, an asshole Russian who drove for Yellow Taxi, got out of his cab and started yelling toward the men in the blue shirts.

"HEY CONVICTS, NEED A RIDE? CONVICTS, HEY CONVICTS, NEED A RIDE? GOT YOUR TAXI RIGHT HERE, HEY CONVICTS, CONVICTS!"

Val knew they would not retaliate for fear of getting sent right back to jail. I secretly wished one of these men would get in Val's cab one day and strangle him with his own seat belt.

The convicts lingered for a few minutes and then dispersed on foot into the hot bowels of downtown.

An old drunk wearing only one shoe came stumbling through the parking lot of the Greyhound toward our cabs. When he was about 50 yards away, he fell flat on his face. Little John jumped out of his cab and ran over to the guy. Little John bent down and helped the guy up and then the guy tried to hit him in the jaw. Little John pushed him off and the guy fell down again, stood up, fell again, then stood up a final time and stumbled away toward Broadway.

Little John walked back to his cab.

"Some people just don't want help," he said.

"Did you ask him if he had any weed?" I said.

"Don't joke about it," he said.

"Something will come up."

"Shit, I got to get out of this city. I got to get back to the country. I was raised in the country, you know."

He lit a cigarette.

"We used to have chickens, goats, pigs, all that," he continued. "That was the fucking life, better than this shitty city. This place is fucking dirty, man, and full of assholes. Plus, in the country, you can grow your own weed."

"So, what's stopping you?" I said.

"I don't know. I've got my apartment. Besides, how would I get money?"

A Greyhound bus pulled into the station and emptied itself of people. A few of the cabs in the front of the queue got fares and pulled away. All the cabs moved 15 yards up.

"I had this one little chicken," Little John said, "on the farm. Little fuzzy yellow thing, and she grew attached to me. I named her Peepers. Damn, she was cute, man; you should have seen her. She followed me around everywhere I went."

81

"How old were you?" I said.

"I was like eight or nine, I think, yeah. Shit, Peepers, I haven't thought about her in a long time. But it's sad, though, because one day we were running through a field, and I was running real fast, you know, and I guess she just couldn't take it and she stopped. I felt bad and went back and bent over her and she was breathing real heavy and kind of twitching in the grass. Jesus, I started crying. And then you know what happened?"

"What?"

"Her heart exploded. It fucking exploded right out of her chest. Right out of her little fucking chest."

I gave him a look of disbelief.

"I'm serious, it did. It exploded right out of her chest. There was blood on the ground; it was terrible."

Tears slid down his cheeks. He looked away and wiped them with his sleeve.

"Maybe you should just stay here in the city, big fella," I said.

He shook his head up and down, but he couldn't talk anymore. Another bus wasn't scheduled to arrive for an hour.

"I've got to go," I said. "I've got a personal fare."

"Ain't you lucky."

I pulled out, to the delight of the cab driver behind me. I didn't have a personal fare, but I wanted to move. Everything starts with moving: just keep moving and the luck would change. It was like death just sitting there.

I drove over to the Food City by Randolph Park and got a Sonoran-style hot dog at an outdoor stand. A Mexican guy handed it to me and it was loaded: beans, jalapeño sauce, mayo, mustard, onions, tomatoes, and bacon.

I was standing there eating the steaming hot dog next to my cab in the bright sun when I saw a man running toward me across the Food City parking lot, waving his arm. He was lugging a suitcase and it was obvious he needed a cab. *Come to papa,* I thought. His face was red and it looked like his heart would burst from his chest.

RAMIREZ

A photo shop is an okay place to work, I guess. At the one where I work, we process film and print pictures. We guarantee to do this within one hour, but in truth, this isn't a big challenge. What makes this photo shop special is that we will develop your homemade pornography. I think this is the only shop left in town that will do it.

Film replete with nudity is, you could say, what we here at One-Hour Photo live for. Luckily, this is a college town. The most that can be expected with any regularity are the old standards: "college girl surprised by roommate in the midst of ablution," "drunken flash of tan-lined breasts," and so many moons you'd think they were stars.

But sometimes I am rewarded with the genuine article. In fact, I got lucky just the other day. A college girl handed me a real grassroots effort. 36 exposures and not once had the camera ventured out of her dorm room. It was awkward when she returned to the shop an hour later, pink-skirted and fresh, to pick up her packet of photographs, inside of which, I was thinking as I handed it to her, were dozens of images of herself in varying degrees of labia-exposing contortionism. Standing like an ape draped over the cash register, I mumbled "$8.32" while visualizing her virginal mouth around the cock of some victoriously faceless frat boy, her eyes gazing up into the camera for validation. She dug into her purse for money. The awkwardness is trivial when weighed against the substance it lends to my weary days.

This amusement, however, has arrived at an unforeseen contingence. It involves a character I refer to simply as Ramirez. I speak it with my diaphragm lowered, as if I am uttering something foul.

Ramirez...

Ramirez walked into our photo shop one day about a year and a half ago. He was driving a yellow cab and he double-parked it out front. He carried with him the first of dozens of disposable cameras, which, it turned out, had no other purpose than to enlarge the visual archives of his sex life. To fully appreciate this, let me describe Ramirez. He's around 55, domed with a reflective skull on which a few greasy tendons of hair meander between liver spots the size of railroad track pennies. His belly is so cumbersome it often obscures the very penis he is trying to capture on film. He walks with a shuffling gate, and has a wind about him of degenerative tissue.

The snapshots of his ridiculous copulations are made doubly carnivalistic when you consider the women he abducts for these "shoots" are prostitutes of the lowest order. It was obvious he found them in the filthiest corners of the city while he drove his cab. Fat, imbecile-faced wretches or track-marked, black-eyed skeletons have been Ramirez's bill of fare once a week ever since.

I have always enjoyed a good laugh over old Ramirez and his habit of historical record.

But everything changed two weeks ago. Ramirez entered our little shop as usual, except he seemed different somehow. There was a gleam in his eye. And there was a smile on his face instead of his characteristic sneer. And he was talkative. He set his film on the counter while I grabbed an order form and wrote his name automatically.

"You may've noticed," he said, clearing his throat, "I have a little, uh, hobby."

"As a matter of fact, I did," I said.

Then he smiled and walked out the door. For Ramirez, that was talkative. It was the longest conversation we ever had.

I put his film into the processor. Machines do all the work, I just keep the fluids up. While I waited, I kept thinking about Ramirez's odd manner. When the negative strip was ready to be fed into the viewer, I set it up and waited for the first frame to appear on the little screen.

When it jumped into sight, I nearly capsized my chair. What should I see but old whale-bellied Ramirez, his willowy manhood worming into the mouth of a girl who appeared to all the world to be a college coed. There was no wrinkle, blemish, scar, bruise, or imperfection anywhere, and that includes the tiny, poignantly erotic face. Nothing was hidden. She was thin, except at necessary, luxurious areas, and soft all over. She was not violated by any metal balls or studs. She had no tattoos. Not a trace of hair existed anywhere aside from the thick gleaming auburn river that flowed nearly to the crack of her soul.

I dismissed the idea that she was another prostitute when, after excruciating examination, there surfaced not a shred of evidence of a condom, which is unique among all of Ramirez's previous dalliances. He was always careful; I'll say that for him.

Maybe she was crazy? Well, it seemed to me that all women were crazy. Besides, her comeliness rendered that irrelevant.

It made me crazy just to look at her.

It was out of this world. The more I thought about it, the more it bothered me. The wheels of logic and natural law spun to their snapping points. I consider myself okay looking, a normal guy, and yet (and here we arrive at the crux of the matter) I find myself currently leading a life of despotic celibacy. I've been alone ever since I started working at this damn job two-and-a-half years ago. And then here's Ramirez, Old Stinky, despoiling this doe before my very eyeballs. Moreover, she appears to be enjoying it. She wants it. She doesn't mind also that he is taking pictures of her everywhere and throughout every moment of it with an off-brand disposable camera. Dumb-assed Ramirez holds the camera extended in his hand at arm's length and tries to achieve the angles. He likes to see himself, I assume. When the intensity builds to a predictable level, he tends to lose form, and sometimes there's only an eye or half of a nipple or just the bedroom dresser.

He must have quite a collection by now, dozens of these X-rated still-lives stacked in trunks and boxes in his reeking closet. Proof.

Ramirez...

It's as if he brings these images to me to flaunt them, to lord them. It's as if he senses how much I hate him and envy him. It's as if he knows something I don't.

It gets worse: he started bringing film nearly every day, for almost two weeks now. Always the same girl in the pictures. Where did all the monsters go? What's happened to the world?

Ramirez...

It's a sad thing, but funny, too. Is it a miracle?

I keep telling myself he needs me because I'm the only place in town that will develop his film. But deep down, I know I need him at least as much as he needs me. Probably more.

WHAT'S GOING TO HAPPEN TO ME?

I'm dispatched in my taxi to pick a lady up at Northwest Hospital. When I pull up, I see a Mexican woman standing by a white lady in a wheelchair, but I don't stop. I don't want her to be the one. There's something about the look on the white lady's face, a look of hatred and judgment and entitlement that I have seen so many times, and the Mexican woman standing there looking lost and sad.

I do a loop around the hospital and then come back around and they're still there.

"Mrs. Buckner?" I say out the window, and they both nod.

"It's about time, where the hell you been?"

She can't be older than 50.

"Traffic," I say.

"I'll have your job."

"Take it," I say. "It's yours."

She says to the Mexican lady, "Where's my purse? Don't you have my fucking purse?"

"You must have left it inside," the Mexican lady says.

"I didn't leave it anywhere! YOU must have left it inside. Well, go get it! And keep your grubby mitts out of it, too! I know how much money I have in there!"

The Mexican woman tells the old lady in the wheelchair: "Don't move, I'll go get it." She runs inside the hospital. She's at least 15 years older than the white lady.

The white lady starts to wheel herself out of the shade toward the curb, but she can't control the wheelchair on the slope and she goes sailing down the sidewalk over the curb and into the parking lot. She does a faceplant on the pavement and lays there wailing and squirming.

I jump out of my cab as the Mexican lady runs out of the hospital with the old lady's bag. A bunch of nurses run out after her and gather around the old lady to pick her up. Her face is bleeding, but not too bad. Her screams seem more angry and accusatory than from real pain, like none of it is her fault, like nothing has ever been her fault.

They stand her up. Her legs work as she shakes off the nurses. She's as strong as Jim Thorpe! She leaps back into the wheelchair. It is clear by the reactions of the nurses that the lady isn't seriously injured.

The Mexican woman tries to soothe the white lady.

"Get away from me! And give me my purse!"

She snatches the purse and the nurses wheel her into the hospital. I walk up to the Mexican woman. She is the lady's caregiver and it is her first job since becoming legalized in the United States. She's only had the job for three days. She's crying quietly.

"What's going to happen to me?"

She'll lose her job, for sure. There might be a lawsuit; she might get sent back to Mexico. She has family here and in Mexico who depend on her, a family who lives in poverty the likes of which the white woman can't imagine and certainly can't sympathize with.

It's hot standing there in the sun and we can still hear the old lady screaming from inside. God help me, I want to walk in there and slap her.

I feel guilty walking away back to my cab, but they don't need a ride now, and I have my own problems. I call dispatch to tell them to give me something else. It's that point in the day, around noon, when all the shadows disappear.

DO I LOOK LIKE AN INDIAN TO YOU?

Women never want to tell you their age until they pass the age of 85, and then they tell you every five minutes. I had old Charlotte in my cab the other day, 95 years young. She still walks pretty good with a cane. Four feet nine inches tall, rat nest red wig crooked on her head. We got in the cab. She's an old New York Jewish lady, too ornery to die.

"What's going on, Charlotte?"

"What?"

"HOW ARE YOU?"

"Oh, I'm fine, I turned 95 last month."

"Yes, I know. Did your son take you out to eat?"

"My son? He's 65 years old, and STILL on that diet! He took me out to eat on my birthday, but he wouldn't eat any cake."

"Where did he take you?"

"What was it? Zara's? Zaba's? Zaria's?"

"I don't know. Was it an Indian place?"

"What?"

"WAS IT AN INDIAN PLACE?"

"Indian? Do I look like an Indian to you?"

"No, sorry."

"It was a good place; we had falafel. It was good falafel."

"Where was it?"

"It was someplace off Grant."

"Grant and Country Club?"

"No..."

"Grant and Campbell?"

"No. It was after Campbell; what's the next street after that?"

"Tucson Boulevard?"

"No..."

"Country Club?"

"Yes! That's it; it was Grant and Country Club!"

"Well, that sounds like a nice place."

"It was. I had falafel and a Coke. My son didn't have a Coke; he had water."

"Because of his diet?"

"No. What's that got to do with it? He just doesn't like Coke."

THE MAZE

He's in my cab for ten minutes when he mentions his hairless cat. I had picked him up at the Circle K on 10th and Perkins. Old, skeletal man.

"You should see this thing," he says. "No hair at all. Not even whiskers."

"Not even whiskers?"

"Not a single one. People think I cut them off, but I would NEVER DO THAT. They just never grew in."

"I'll be darned."

"I have to put a shirt on her when I take her outside or else she'll sunburn. If I leave her out there too long, she gets sunburn marks on her arms where the shirt stops, like a farmer. Her head, too."

"Poor little gal."

"I put sunblock on her once, but she licked it off and threw up all over the place. You wanna see her?"

He pulls a photograph from his wallet and shows it to me.

"Here she is. Here's my Fluffy."

I glance at the photograph. It's him holding this cat. He's sitting on a lawn chair. It's true: it appears to be completely hairless.

"I wonder what the point of not having hair is," I say.

"It's an ancient breed. The Peruvians bred them and kept them in their pyramids. They're very spiritual, very close to God."

"That makes sense."

"I take baths with her sometimes. She's not afraid of water; she just gets right in with me."

"Is that safe?"

"She doesn't scratch me. At first I was worried about the old satchel, but she's never scratched me. She loves the water. That's another characteristic of the breed. I'm gonna breed her as soon as I can find a male. I contacted a lady in town; I met her on the Internet. She says she has a male, but I'm not sure. She seems kind of crazy."

"Gotta be careful these days."

"I want to breed her and sell the kittens. They go for $1,500 a piece."

"Jesus!"

"You know anyone that wants one?"

"Not off-hand."

"I can offer a cabbie discount."

"I'll ask around."

"Hey, here's my trailer, turn in here. You want to come in and see Fluffy? She doesn't get much company. The other cats in the neighborhood pick on her, so I have to keep her isolated most of the time."

"That's okay, I gotta get going. Gotta make money, you know."

He looks sad at this news.

"Oh," he says. "Okay. You're the first cab driver who hasn't wanted to come in and see her. All the other cab drivers have come in to have a look at her. She's very affectionate. One cab driver even took a photo and sent it to his wife."

"Maybe I'll just take a raincheck."

"You don't like cats?"

"I like cats."

"She's not sick or nothin'. She looks strange, but it's normal in her case."

"No disrespect intended, it's just that I got some bills that need to be paid and I'm kind of in a hurry..."

"Okay..." he says. He pays and gets out.

The curtain moves in the front window of his trailer like there's a wind inside, but outside, it's calm. The hair on the back of my neck stands up. I scrape the front of my cab backing out of his driveway. Then I take the wrong street in the trailer park trying to get out. It's like a test, trying to find the exit, almost like there's somebody watching me from above, making notes.

FUN WITH RUBY

Ruby Dalton is 94 years old. I like to fuck with her when I pick her up in my taxi. She hates the freeway. I know this from the many times I've driven her from here to there on her state-paid vouchers, usually to the senior center for bingo or sometimes to the grocery store. Today, I pick her up at her house and she climbs in. She still lives on her own. I put her walker in the trunk and get moving.

"You want me to take the freeway?" I say.

"NO FREEWAY!" she says. "It's too far west! I suppose if you ENJOY going miles and miles out of your way, then go ahead! Take the freeway! You're the driver! You're the one driving, not me! What do I know? I'm just a stupid old lady!"

"Okay, I'll take La Cholla."

"Why don't you take La Cholla!"

"I'll do that, ma'am."

When we get to La Cholla, I get in the left turn lane and sit there with my blinker on and wait for the traffic to let me turn.

"HEY! TURN HERE! This is La Cholla!" she yells from the back.

"You mean this street right here?"

"THIS IS LA CHOLLA, TURN HERE!"

"Right or left?"

"LEFT! How old are you, anyway? Where'd you get your license, a Cracker Jack box?"

When we get to the senior center, I help her out and get her walker and ask her, "Do you need me to walk you to the door?"

"No, I'll be all right."

"Okay, bye now."

As I begin walking away, she says, "I know it's stated in your contract you're supposed to walk us to the door! Last week, one of YOU GUYS left Mildred to walk by herself and she fell and broke her hip!"

"Okay, I'll walk you to the door."

"I mean, unless you're in a big hurry or something, unless you've got to run, if it wouldn't be TOO MUCH trouble."

Later in the day, I happen to get the call to take her home. One of those days. I go in to the senior center and walk her out to the cab. We get all settled.

"So," I say, "you want me to take the freeway?"

PORTRAIT OF THE ARTIST AS A CERTIFIED LOONY

I receive a fare from my cab's computer monitor, a $10 voucher. I've transported the woman before. She's on disability because she's too crazy to work. Plus, she's an artist. She's very creative, which is why she can't hold a job. 38 years old, tanned, fit, well dressed. But the stress is killing her.

I pull into her driveway where she lives with her mother, a saint, I'm sure. The house is a half-million-dollar job up in the foothills. She comes walking from around the back of the house carrying two buckets full of mesquite branches. I don't question. I put the mesquite branches in the hatchback of the cab. The branches are too long for the hatchback to close. I begin breaking them in half to make them fit. Then she comes back with two more buckets of mesquite branches and I do the same with them.

"I'll be right back," she says and runs into the house.

I get all the mesquite branches broken down and close the hatchback and wait.

Five minutes, ten minutes...15 minutes. I stand outside the cab. A hummingbird comes near me and studies my red shirt. What's up, little fella? He zips away. Maybe he was a she.

I walk to the door of the house, knock, no answer. Every minute I wait is lost money for me, lost time. What the hell? How did I get here? *Appreciate every moment of life*, I think. *Gonna die anyway*, I think. Why worry?

Finally, she comes out.

"I have to go," I say.

"Just a couple more minutes!" she says.

"Is this a game?" I say.

"Okay!" she screams. "Maybe I won't even go today! I don't think I can ride with you if you are going to be so rude. I will be moving from Tucson tomorrow and you'll never have to see me again! You'll like that, won't you? You'll be really happy then!"

"Jesus," I say.

Then she comes over and gets in the cab. I drive in silence to this place she's going to, a pottery studio. She gets on her cell phone and starts texting, texting, texting...finally, she finishes.

"I just made a complaint about you to your company," she says. "Good luck having a job tomorrow."

"Hurray," I say.

We get to the pottery studio, Fort Lowell and Alvernon. Tiny parking lot, designed by an idiot. I unload her buckets of mesquite branches as she runs up to a woman in a tie-dyed shirt and embraces her. The sisterhood.

When I drive off, she gives me the middle finger. Then she picks up a mesquite stick and throws it at my cab. She throws like an artist: misses me by 30 feet. I give her a beep of the horn and zip away, off to search for flowers and nectar before I kiss the big one.

TURN AROUND, DUMBASS

I got a call yesterday in my taxi, 409 W. Rudasil Road. I was about five miles away and I dialed the phone number to let the person know I was on my way. A tough guy voice answers, no "hello," just this: "Turn around, dumbass, you drove right past me."

"Pardon? This is Matt from Discount Cab."

"No shit, 'Matt,' you drove right past me."

"I'm five miles away from you, sir; you must have seen a different taxi. There are several of us."

"Oh, then hurry up, I'm late."

I pull up 13 minutes later and he's standing by the road with a suitcase.

"Airport," he says as he gets in. 52-year-old white guy who was pissed off he wasn't a millionaire yet.

I know from experience that assholes like this have their own special route to go to the airport, and if you don't go that route they will make a stink about it, but I also know if you ASK them what route they want to use, they will assume you are so stupid you don't even know how to get to the airport and they will abuse you for that, too.

I ask him, "I usually go down Oracle to Miracle Mile and then to the freeway, but do you want to go another way?"

Big, BIIIIGGGG sigh from the back seat.

"Jesus!" he says. "Just go down Oracle to Grant, take a RIGHT ON GRANT, get on the FREEWAY, and then go down to the Park exit."

"The Park exit? Not the Kino exit?"

"Shit! The Kino exit is THE LONG WAY! Do you even know how to drive this thing?"

"What town are we in anyway?"

"Fuck! I knew I should have called an Uber!"

I head down Oracle.

After a few minutes, he says, "Take Miracle Mile. Miracle Mile is faster."

"Whatever you say, boss."

"Unless you just prefer a hundred stop lights," he says. "Miracle Mile is faster."

"By God, you're right."

On the freeway, he keeps staring at the speedometer to make sure I'm going at least eight MPH over the limit.

"Where you flying off to?" I say.

"Why, you writing a book?"

"Memoirs."

I take the Park exit off the freeway. It's a dumb way to go to the airport; two more stop lights, slower speed limit. But we get there.

"$23," I say.

"I should get a discount," he says.

"And I should have never gotten out of prison," I say.

"Now you know where the airport is," he says, tossing the bills on the passenger seat. "You're welcome."

RED BULL BLUES

He gets in the cab outside the apartment complex. He's maybe 25 years old. His fingernails are long and filthy and he's wearing $90 jeans.

"Take me to the Northwest hospital," he says. "ER. Shit, I just came home a couple of hours ago and found my wife on the floor. The ambulance came and they said I could ride with them, but when I went to get my coat, they fucking left me. I mean, she's been depressed lately, but I didn't think she'd go this far. Her doctor gave her pills for her depression and she fucking took the whole bottle."

"Oh, man," I say, "I'm sorry."

"Fuck, the holidays, you know?"

"Yeah."

"Hey, is there a mini-mart we can stop at? I need a Red Bull. I don't want to fall asleep."

"Sure, there's one on the corner here."

I pull in and he gets out. I can see him through the window of the mini-mart; he goes up to the counter, then apparently forgets something and runs back to an aisle and comes back to the counter again. Then he points and I can see the cashier pulling out some lottery scratch-offs. He stands there and scratches them off while a couple of other people stand behind him in line. He comes out.

And I take him to the hospital.

THE GREAT DESERT PALMS ESCAPE

I pulled my cab into the long, smooth driveway that led to Desert Palms, a high-end rehab/loony bin out in the middle of nowhere. It was getting close to Christmas and they had put little Santa hats on the saguaro cacti. Before I could get to the front gate, a guy jumped out of the mesquite bushes and leapt in front of my cab. He was wearing a white smock and his black hair was all over the place. He looked like he was about 30.

He got into the cab and ducked down out of sight.

"Get me the FUCK out of here," he said.

"Wait," I said, checking the order on the computer screen. "Are you J. Pipple?"

"Yes, for Chrissakes, just move!"

"Where to?"

"The closest bar."

"Dressed like that?"

"You're right. Take me to Target first."

"You got money?"

"This place costs 2,000 bucks a day, dude. I got money."

"I mean, do you have money ON you?"

He pulled his wallet out and waved it at me.

"GO, man!"

I flipped a bitch and got out to the main road. He relaxed a bit then.

"I must have been crazy to check myself into that place," he said. "It's supposed to be voluntary, you know, just to clean up and relax a little, eat some good food, massages, steam room, you know. They got some hot nurses, too."

"Hold on," I said. "Two THOUSAND a day?"

"Yep. I got the deluxe package."

"What do you do for a living?"

"I'm in real estate. My dad owns half the East Side."

"Don't try anything funny. I'm packin' heat."

"You're not packin' shit. Calm down. You're kind of paranoid, aren't you?"

"I've had a rough week."

"YOU'VE had a rough week? Check this shit out. That fucking place back there is supposed to be voluntary. Well, I'm in there a week and one day they have a barbecue for all the patients. Hamburgers and hot dogs and tofu dogs and stuff. They had some Chippendales boy toy cooking the hamburgers. He was all done up in cowboy attire, big hat, chaps, I swear. All the ladies were creaming their panties. The nurses, too. Whatever, the hamburgers were good. But one of the rules is you're not supposed to take food to your room, I mean, unless you're diabetic. Fuck that. I put three hamburgers in my coat pocket. Big juicy things; I swear it was ground ribeye. Well, as I'm walking back to my room, there's this basketball court there, and I cut across it. It was getting to be dusk and suddenly there's this fucking coyote standing right in front of me. He's looking all dodgy and eyeing me and shit. I turn and there's ANOTHER one. Then behind me, I heard a third one. THREE motherfucking coyotes! And they weren't going anywhere. I tried to push my way through them and they started circling me. It freaked me out and I started yelling, HELP, HELP! A couple of the nurses ran over. That's when I realized they smelled the hamburger. The coyotes, I mean, not the nurses. I pulled the hamburgers out and threw them and they fucking pounced on those motherfuckers. Then I got the hell back to my room."

"Beats the hell out of jackrabbit, I bet."

"Yeah, so, anyway, word got out about the hamburgers. I was in big trouble. They took my clothes away and gave me this fucking smock.

I was not to be trusted with pockets of any kind. And I heard through the grapevine that they were planning on having me committed to Kino downtown. Can you believe that shit?"

"Which Target you want to go to?"

"The one on Oracle's fine."

"$2,000 a fucking day, wow."

"Yeah, there were some real big shots there. Martin Sheen was there."

"No shit?"

"No shit. He was all fucked up. I guess it runs in the family. He hopped out a window one night and jumped the fence and hitchhiked his way all the way to Phoenix. He'd smuggled some drugs in with him. But he came back the next day."

"Martin Sheen, that's something else. He made a good president."

"That's what gave me the idea: Martin Sheen jumping out of a window like that. I called a taxi and got the hell out of there. They were gonna send me to fucking KINO, man. You ever been to Kino?"

"Just the lobby. There was a lot of moaning and yelling. It smelled strange, too."

"That smell is bleach and boiled brains. Kino is the bottom of the barrel, man; that's where they send the hard cases. You go into that place and it's bye bye, birdy."

"I'll bet it doesn't cost two grand a day."

"Hey, you think you could go into Target and buy me a pair of pants and a shirt? I don't want to go in there wearing this fucking smock."

"Can I get a soft pretzel?"

"Sure. Get me one, too."

"Okay."

"Any good bars around here?"

"Strip club down the road a-ways."

"Awesome. Seriously, dude, you saved my life."

"Merry Christmas."

BITCOIN

New Year's Day 2016, 4:33 AM. I picked up a guy in my cab, a young hipster dude. He said he'd been up all night building web sites. He's a web designer, freelance, yeah, pretty cool, he's doing really well. He wanted to go down to an all-night coffee shop, said he was gonna buy some "Bitcoin" from a guy there. He couldn't believe I'd never heard of Bitcoin.

"Bitcoin is the only currency you can rely on these days," he told me. "It's a kind of crypto money, so when the whole system goes to pot and the dollar is worthless, people with Bitcoin won't have to worry."

"What if the computers go down with the whole system?" I asked.

He chuckled.

"Well, if you're in-the-know, you have a backup," he told me. "I could explain it to you, but we don't have the time."

I took him down to the all-night coffee shop and he wanted me to wait for him. In a few minutes, he came out smiling. Then I took him back home.

At his apartment building, he tried to pay the cab fare with his debit card. The card was declined. It said "insufficient funds." He pulled out another and that was declined, too, message reading, "Do not honor."

"I don't accept Bitcoin, sorry," I said.

He said he'd be right back with some money, hopped out, and ran into his apartment. He never came back. I could have called the cops, but the last time I did that, they didn't show up for three hours. I could have pounded on his door and played the tough guy, but I didn't have the energy for that. I just said fuck it and drove away. $28 in the hole to start the new year.

I turned the radio to the George Strait marathon on 99.5 and hoped the world wouldn't end before they played "How 'Bout Them Cowgirls."

AT LEAST IT ISN'T RAINING

Dispatchers and cab drivers are always at each others' throats. The dispatchers think of themselves as "management," even though the drivers make more money. Cab drivers are constantly correcting dispatch errors and never get credit for it, and the dispatchers are rarely held accountable for their errors. If a cab driver makes an error, the driver loses money. If a dispatcher makes an error, the driver loses money.

I pull up to an apartment house and call the phone number. Miraculously, it's the right number.

"Your cab's out front."

"Be right there," a lady says.

In a few minutes, she comes wheeling down the sidewalk on a motorized wheelchair. Her legs are all shriveled up; she's obviously been this way since birth.

"Why'd they send a car?" she says. "I need a wheelchair van."

"They screwed up."

"They always do this!"

"I know. Let me call them."

I call the dispatch number and get put on hold for nine minutes. Me and the lady in the wheelchair just kind of look at each other and roll our eyes. I get a girl on the phone.

"What can I do for you, cab 1812?"

"This customer needs a wheelchair van."

"She needs a van?"

"She needs a WHEELCHAIR van."

"Well," she snickers, "same thing."

"No, it's not. We have regular vans and we have wheelchair vans."

"She's never ordered a wheelchair van before. What's the problem?"

"What do you think is the problem?"

"No need to get snippy, sir."

"She's right here in front of me, and she's in a wheelchair and she needs a wheelchair van."

"Is it a foldable wheelchair? Can't you just put it in the trunk?"

"No!"

"Calm down or I will be forced to disconnect and report you. I can see that she's taken cabs four times this month, never a wheelchair van. Ask her."

"Have you been taking wheelchair vans or regular cars this month?" I ask the lady, already knowing the answer.

"I have never taken a regular car, I need a WHEELCHAIR VAN!"

"She cannot use anything but a wheelchair van. Your information is wrong," I say to the dispatcher.

"It's all right here on the screen, sir. Ask her where she's going."

"What? What's that got to do with it? Here, talk to her yourself."

I hand the phone to the lady in the wheelchair. She puts the phone to her ear and then says, "Hello? Okay, then why did he give the phone to me?"

She hands the phone back to me.

"I don't want to talk to her, sir!" the dispatcher says. "I can't send her a wheelchair van. She needs to call her insurance or something. Ask her if she has insurance."

"Oh my God! Look, take me off this call! What do you think I'm supposed to do about it?"

"No need to raise your voice, sir. Okay, I'm cancelling you off the call.

I'm breaking protocol now, you know. According to the rules, you have expressed an interest in this call and if you do not perform the call after making contact with the customer, you can be suspended for 30 minutes."

"BUT I CANNOT TRANSPORT THE CUSTOMER, SHE NEEDS A WHEELCHAIR VAN."

"So you say. People lie, sir. Have a good day."

She hangs up and takes me off the call. The whole thing has wasted 40 minutes of my time which I will never be compensated for.

"What about me?" the lady in the wheelchair says.

"Sorry, I guess you're gonna have to call and try again."

"Fuck!" she says. "Pardon my French."

"It's okay," I say.

"At least it isn't raining," she says.

MARSHMALLOWS ON EVERYTHING

Christmas Day: what a pitchfork of horseshit. I have that feeling that I blew it again, that there is something wrong. My boss June threw me the guilt trip all week until I said okay, I'll come to your Christmas ham. I am a cab driver and June is the owner of the cab company. The strings of little lights blink red and green and white and red and green and white. No snow in Too-Stoned, Arizona. Boo hoo. Thank God. If you want snow, you know the road that leads to the mountains. Relationships require constant care. People have egos. There's something wrong with them. I have no children or wife, and this means I am at their beck and call. They think: the old boy doesn't have anything else to do, he's lonely, he's a corner-filler, he'll clog some low-rent space, he'll be a good time, round out the photos, nibble on the potatoes, smile. Haw! What fun! Sing and dance! Dance and sing! Pretend to love each other. Pretend to know what love is! Pretend to care.

Parties. People. Jesus. There's something wrong with this. I don't want to hang out with the puke-faces I work with. Who would? The meth-mouths, the crackheads, the criminals. Cab drivers are scum. I'm sorry. I need to make money in order to pay the rent and to survive. I need a job. I need to be decent. I only have a few quality hours per week free for myself.

Cab drivers have breath like a cat's litterbox. I have a mother who is far away. And a father? He doesn't trust religion. He doesn't trust anything except physical sensations, because he can feel them, and emotions, because he can feel them.

I touch the gate—cold metal on my hand—and June's dog greets me. Honeybear! Good clean warm smile with tongue hanging out pink and wet and naked. She likes to chase the shadow of your hand. I box into the air and she chases the fist-shadows. I hop around and she pounces here, pounces there, mouth open, smiling, pure joy.

I knock on the door and go inside. Inside, it is warm with the smell of food. In this constant stuff-yer-face land, the great yearly feast loses some of its draw. Another idea blown to smithereens. Besides, I can't eat in the presence of others. Sure, I can nibble. I nibble. I lose my appetite. My stomach growls, but if a piece of food touches my tongue, it just sits there. I smile and say, "Wonderful," but really, it just sits there and I just sit there. I chew, mouth closed, jaw going round and round, mechanical. I go for the wine. I can't taste a thing. I'm careful on the way to my mouth. I swallow. Slowly I swallow and smile and put my thumb in the air. Yummers! Jimminny, mmmmmmmmhmmm. More? Hell yeah! Pile it on, atta girl cowgirl, pile it on, hills of it, mountain ranges of it! Instant mashed potatoes. Turkey dry as a bicycle seat. Oranges and marshmallow salad. Burnt orange colored yams sticky as baby crap. Marshmallows melted on top. More marshmallows! Marshmallows on everything! Shit-n-shinola, love me some marshmallows! Can't get enough! And gelatin molds that shine and jiggle and quiver like prairie dogs on a cold windy night, little marshmallows suspended inside like hearts that have stopped beating.

The other day, June telephoned me, crying. She was sniffling and could hardly say three consecutive words without choking up. Her husband had moved out of the house after he'd confessed to several dozen sexual affairs over the last five years. She was through with him, through with him! The slut! The bimbo slut! Momma's tit was dried up, she said. That motherfucker can just see how it is to be on his own! That whore-fuck! I can't believe it, she said. I can't believe it. 17 years, I've known him since he was 22. He was a baby. His mother really fucked him up. But I fixed him! I thought I did. I thought I fixed him. I didn't fix shit! He had sex with Alesia. Alesia! I loved him. Oh my God, I hate him!

I walk into June's house for her Xmas dinner and there is her husband standing there. Nobody else is here. I'm early. I'm always early. What is the husband doing here? His name is Mark; he's a greasy smile. There's something creepy about him, like he'd diddle a little boy if he had the chance. It's hard to put your finger on it. He's not right. He only laughs at his own jokes. That's one of his constants.

June is shaped like a snowman. There is a glass aquarium by the window and she sprays water from a bottle through the top of the aquarium, which is a screen. Inside the aquarium is a green lizard with bulging eyes and a fin on top of his head like a shark's. The lizard sways side to side and seems to be enjoying the spray bottle. A tropical rain! He slowly moves up a small piece of a branch that has been broken off and placed in the aquarium for him. His feet are made for gripping and his tiny toes wrap slowly and tightly around the thin branch as he noses through the leaves. I stand there and stare at the lizard with bulging eyes.

"Do you want to watch TV?" June says. There's no one else here but the three of us and the lizard. None of the other cab drivers have shown up yet. That's why I came early. But the food isn't ready. Nothing is ready.

"No thanks," I say.

"Want a beer?" she says.

"Sure."

She gets me a beer. I open it and drink. It's cold and bitter. It's quiet.

"Oh!" June says. "I almost forgot!"

She runs to the stereo and turns on Xmas music.

"Xmas music!" she says.

I sit on the couch.

"Do you want to surf the Internet?" June says.

"Hey!" her husband Mark cries. "I was going to use it!" He wants to use the Internet. What is going on? June has forgiven him. It's Christmas and June has forgiven him.

June goes into the kitchen to work on the grub. The smells are good but I can hardly breathe. I look at Mark. He sits at the computer. The slut. The beer splashes in my stomach.

"You gotta see this," Mark says.

I stand up and walk over and look over his shoulder. He's looking at a website advertising a group of citizen-militia who call themselves the Minutemen. They live along the Mexican border here in Arizona and their aim is to prevent illegal Mexican immigrants from trespassing on their private, God-given, grandpa-given property. Gold-booted ranchers, mostly. Self-righteous and paranoid.

115

"We gotta keep America the way it is," Mark says.

"What way is that?"

"I don't want no wetback Mexican telling me what to do," he says. "Next thing, we'll be eating tamales for Christmas dinner."

"I like tamales," I say.

"Hey, do you know why Mexicans make tamales for Christmas?"

"No."

"So they'll have something to open on Christmas morning!"

He doubles over with laughter, then straightens.

"Pretty soon they'll run the whole show," he says.

He scowls at me.

"Where were you born?" he says.

"Peoria, Illinois," I say.

"Oh," he says, disappointed. He was thinking I might be a wetback. He turns back to his Minutemen. He's got ideas. He's going to join the Minutemen and keep the Mexicans out of the U.S.A., which will ensure that everything will be perfect forever. He doesn't even have a ranch to protect. He's nothing but a slut cab driver. But he's got ideas. Save the world. Solve the world. Keep the world. Keep the world as it is. It's a good world.

June is still in the kitchen, humming. A snowman humming and gliding around, a snowman that had called me crying, broken down, three days earlier. My stomach sinks in and sucks out. It's a trap! It feels like a trap. Guilt. There's emotion for you! Running up your arm like a rat! A roach across the counter. Blam, blam! Bullets of light, and it zips to some crevice.

I think of Virginia, the girl I met in the shoe store. Mexican. Got the long dark hair. You don't think you're gonna meet a girl in a shoe store. She was working there and she helped me find cheap walking shoes. She had a sore on her lip. I asked her if she wanted to meet me after work, and she said yes, and we met at a park and we walked around the park and we talked. She told me I probably didn't want to get involved with her because she had *"muchos problemas."* I fell in love with her. Three laps around the small park, the warm desert summer night, the mesquite flowers making us sneeze. A couple of nights later, we were kissing on her couch in her apartment. She had that sore on her lip, but I didn't care. I had been alone for eight years. A quarter of my life. A week later, she went to Mexico to visit her family for Christmas. I watched her get on the bus. One year ago and she never came back. I went to her apartment and her roommate told me she had been nabbed at the border and could not return. Her roommate said she had no way of contacting Virginia; she had heard the story through the grapevine. She slammed the door on me. A sore came up on my lip soon after that. Now it comes and goes every few months, like a little burnt marshmallow.

I want to kill Mark sitting at the computer. But I save him. I keep him. I keep him the way he is.

I turn around and walk out of June's house and through the sharp-shadowed yard. I open the gate; cold in my hand. I say goodbye to Honeybear. I walk up the road in the sun and step up the stairs, thighs burning, to my apartment door, number 27, and walk through it.

They are perfect for each other, June and Mark. And everyone else. Most everyone else. Who cares? I'm sorry. There's something wrong. It's Christmas, leave me alone.

MERMAID WITH DOCTOR'S MASK

Cathy is sick. Her teeth look like pieces of rotten corn. She's 42 years old.

I pull my cab up to the doctor's office and she walks out the front door very slowly. She looks at me with sad eyes above a white cloth mask which covers her mouth and nose.

"It's you," she says.

"Hi, Cathy."

Her hair has thinned and gone gray and then been dyed brown with a cheap, store-bought dye. Her ears have fallen and are sticking almost straight out under the straps of the mask.

"Allergies," she says in a muffled voice.

She asks me not to go down certain roads because of roughness which will aggravate her and hurt her. Any potholes, forget it. I have to take the long way. This means a larger fare on the meter. She smells like urine and talks as if nothing is wrong.

"How's the art going?" I say.

"I've been doing animal portraits," she says. Cathy went to school and got an MFA. That seems like a lifetime ago, but now she has the time and has finally been able to pursue her dream. She gets tears in her eyes when she thinks about it.

She remembers one thing her art teacher told her that she would never forget: art comes from pain. Well, she's had so much pain she's numbed to it. What now? She would contact her art teacher to ask her, but her art teacher got canned for selling drugs to students and kind of fell off the map.

When we get to her house, I help her to the door. She has a pillow the doctor gave her and it is too heavy for her to carry.

In the living room, I put the pillow down and look up at the wall. It is dominated by three large paintings. The paintings are very bright, mainly yellow, and the main subjects are giant green turtles, one turtle per canvas. On the corrugated shell of the middle turtle, a blue mermaid lies curled in the fetal position with her hair flowing back. She could be dead, but I prefer to think she's sleeping. The paintings are so bad they almost make me angry.

"Would you look at that," I say.

She looks at her paintings. She still hasn't taken off her mask.

"I can't use oils or charcoal," she says, "because of my lungs. I use acrylic."

We stand looking at the paintings. My stomach is a pit of uselessness.

"I better go," I say.

She pays the fare and a small tip. Then I'm in the taxi again. I roll the window down to the sunny afternoon, hoping the dispatcher will give me something else, and quick.

MY OTHER JACKET

I came home from driving the cab all day and I couldn't sleep. I didn't want to be in my apartment. I walked around the block with no sidewalks or streetlights. It was a warm desert night.

I came back to my apartment building, an unpainted two-story cinderblock hulk. I walked up the open-air stairs and past the windows of my neighbors, none of whom I knew personally. I got glimpses inside a few windows, but most had their curtains closed. The smell of meth cooking drifted through the air.

Then I heard it: *ker-clack, ker-clack, ker-clack...*

Here came Crutch Boy walking down the dark road. Crutch Boy was around 30 years old, five feet tall with long, blond, greasy hair. I had never seen him without his crutches ever since I moved into that apartment building eight years earlier. He wore his army coat and carried his standard load: 12-pack of beer. He halted every few yards on his crutches to hurl profanities into the air. When he finally got to the stairs of our apartment building, he held the crutches with one hand and the beer with the other and simply leaped up, two at a time, using both legs perfectly.

Crutch Boy sat down in his little chair outside his door. It was 8 o'clock at night and he had his sunglasses on. I walked over to him.

"How's it going?" I said.

"Yeah?" Crutch Boy said.

"What's your name?" I said.

"My name?" Crutch Boy said. "My name, it was Wes before the rivers came and then my mother and that damn bitch until the Walgreens fiasco."

121

"You don't say."

"But I do say so, sir."

"You lived here long?" I said.

"Long?" he said. "Long, long time ago, I saw that giant clown cross the street to go to the outhouse WAY up on Henderson Hill."

"What's new?" I said. "Same old shit, eh?"

"New, never, nothing is new ever," Crutch Boy said. "I got some new shoes once."

A few moments of silence passed while he sat there drinking from his can of beer. He put a pair of headphones on his ears and began to tamp his foot. The headphone wires dangled freely, connected to nothing.

"What're ya listening to?"

"Listening to?" he said. "There's a big fucking bird up there, man, can't you hear it? It's black and blue and stole my jacket."

"But you're wearing your jacket," I said.

"My other jacket."

Lightning appeared in the west. The breeze picked up, wet and smelling of creosote.

"I really don't want company," Crutch Boy said.

"Sure you do."

"No, no, no, no, no!"

"Of course you do."

"Go away," Crutch Boy said. "Go away! GO AWAY, GO AWAY!"

I didn't move. Crutch Boy stood up slowly and grabbed one of his crutches and raised it above his head to hit me.

"Okay, okay," I said. "Take it easy."

I backed away and walked over to my apartment.

"THANK YOU!" Crutch Boy said. "THANK ALL THE GOD IN THE HEAVENS AND LET THE LORD OF SATAN TRY TO GET AWAY WITH THAT AROUND HERE! I SAW HIM! I TOLD HIM NOT TO, BUT HE DID IT ANYWAY, THANK YOU! THANK YOU, THANK

YOU..."

I guess everybody has their crutches. Sometimes it doesn't feel very good to be alive and you can't sleep and you don't know what to do. I stood outside my apartment and leaned on the railing.

LATE

She is the color of dusty coffee. She climbs slowly in the front seat of the cab, all 92 years of her. She has to go to the doctor.

"Good morning, young man," she says. "You're late."

I was five minutes late because of a funeral procession on Oracle. Must have been some big shot drug dealer or something, with all those mourners.

"Sorry," I say.

What's your name?"

"Matt."

"I'm Rowina."

"Nice to meet you, ma'am."

"Matt, I sure hope you're a good driver."

"Don't worry," I say, pulling onto Pima Street.

"Hmmph," she says.

"You don't believe me?"

"Well, I just don't know, do I?" she says. "My husband Edward always said he was a good driver, too, hmmph. One time, he tried to take that corner over by 36th Street, you know the one?"

"Sure."

"Well, he couldn't make it. He crashed it! He walked home and you should have seen him! Whooo, doggy!"

"Boy."

125

"Another time, my Edward throwed Albert, that's my baby, Albert, he throwed Albert out the window when he rolled our old Oldsmobile. Shoot, was I hot! Albert was okay, thank the Lord."

Some asshole is on my bumper, so I give him a look in the rearview. He switches lanes and passes. I turn and look in through his passenger window, but the guy doesn't turn his head. Good.

"Edward was all right?" I say.

"Hmmmph, Edward was all right, yes, though I didn't give no mind about that then. He was too darn stubborn to ever get hurt."

"One time he did kill a boy," she says, "a boy he worked with. They was both drinking and my Edward just did what he always did: got in the car and started driving. He drove that car right into a telephone pole. Poor boy was killed, mmm hmmm. Edward went to jail for a couple of years, but when he got out, he weren't no different. Hmmph."

"Too stubborn," I say.

"Ha, you said it, was that man ever stubborn! Lord, he was something."

I let her off at her doctor and promise to come and get her in an hour. But she looks worried and lost, so I walk her to the door of the doctor's office and encourage her to walk up to the receptionist's desk. Then I wave and leave.

As I'm about to pull onto Wilmot Road, a young girl in a huge purple truck runs the red light there at the intersection and doesn't T-bone me only because I slam the brake pedal into the floorboard. She doesn't even give me a glance; she looks straight ahead, smiling vacantly. Her own mortality has never crossed her mind.

A quarter of a second later, she crashes straight into a car that is trying to make a U-turn. Wherever she's going, she's going be late.

YOU CAN HAVE A SEAT, SIR

In my cab, I will often be called to pick up someone from a medical facility. It happens frequently that when I arrive, the patient/passenger is not ready to leave. Inevitably, the receptionist will tell me, "You can have a seat, sir."

This bothers me. Do I really need to stand there among all the empty chairs in the waiting room and be told to "have a seat?" As if, without being told to have a seat, I might just stand there forever, not quite knowing what to do? I might start spazzing out like a robot under a sprinkler? I might start speaking in tongues to the air conditioning vent? I might start punching myself in the face? Is she really giving me PERMISSION to sit down? Golly, thanks! Very kind of you. Is there a charge? Where's the tip jar? You mean I can sit down just like that? What a country! How about a Bloody Mary, babe! And don't put any of that rabbit food in it, either! How should I sit down? Do I bend my legs first or just kind of flop backwards?

But more than this, what bothers me is the idea the receptionist apparently has that I would really love to just sit down in the doctor's office and wait for my passenger. So comfy! Do I need insurance to plop down here and rest the poor old dogs? Boy howdy! I wish I could just stay here all day! Sitting in a doctor's waiting room is so relaxing! My favorite pastime! Cathartic! Pastoral! Can I come here and hang out on my day off? I've got a vacation coming up, was thinking of the Yucatan peninsula, but maybe we could just come to Doctor Vihensseveá's Proctal Care instead. Maybe I can breathe in real deep and catch every disease that's floating around in here! What's that smell? Loose urine? Carbolic acid? Wonderful! Somebody just sneezed a snot rope! Perfect! Ooooh, there's a TV too! Wi-Fi? No way! Wow, just wow. Don't you dare tell me you have cable! And magazines!

Time! Diabetic Weekly! Somebody pinch me!

I always say, "It's okay, I'll wait outside."

Inevitably, the receptionist looks at me like I've just put my finger in her coffee cup.

BOOK PEOPLE

I am on the freeway in my taxi going the speed limit with a passenger lady reading her book in the back seat. Without warning, a truck darts in front of me. I hit the brakes quick so that the lady and I may live another day and I begin to ease up to give us some space.

The lady in the back seat is startled from her reverie, looks up from her book, and says, "Can you please not follow so close behind that truck? You're making me uncomfortable."

112 DEGREES

I was driving my cab through the parking lot of a monstrous apartment complex yesterday trying to scan the apartment numbers. Where the hell was building 78? Jesus Christ. You can't see shit in this headache desert sun. I drove over a speed bump. It was squishy and soft and the bottom of the cab dragged over it. I thought, *fuck, do I have a flat tire?* Is that speed bump melting from the 109-degree heat? I looked in the rearview mirror and saw a couple of Mexicans running out of an apartment and looking at me angrily. I had driven right over a long roll of carpeting that they had laid out on the pavement. *Lo siento, hombres!*

NO WAY

Costco fares are the pits. Negotiating my cab into the Costco parking lot on Saturday afternoon is like trying to fit a camel into a preacher's asshole. Costco has a gas station, too, three cents cheaper than the other stations, which means if you have a 40-gallon tank, you save $1.20, a complete justification for parking lot warfare. My truck's bigger than your truck! Fuck you! Move up, what you waiting for, Christmas? You stole my hose!

99 percent of the time when I find my Costco fare, it's a punchy grandma wearing a Trump hat wanting to go five bucks down the road with her 90-pack of chicken thighs and 200 rolls of butt-wipes. This time it was a mid-aged woman who had lost her keys in the parking lot. She had unlocked her $60,000 Mercedes, loaded all her crap in there, and *then* lost her keys. White mushroom face Elmer-glued onto a Michelin Man body. She was with a friend, almost a twin. The keys had simply vanished. The two women were exasperated. Life sucks. How could something so terrible have happened to them? One of these Mexicans wandering around probably had something to do with it. How do so many Mexicans get Costco cards? What the flying *fuck* is going on with the world? My fare needed a ride home to get her spare set of keys and a ride back to Costco. 20 bucks, I figured.

On the ride to her condo, she asked me where I was from. They always ask that. They want to make sure I'm not an illegal immigrant.

I said, "Illinois."

She said, "NO WAY! I'm from St. Louis!"

I said, "NO WAY! Last time we visited my mom in Quincy, we went to

St. Louis."

She said, "NO WAY, QUINCY? MY FRIEND LIVES IN QUINCY!"

"NO WAY!"

"YEAH, WAY!"

I said, "Well, last time I visited Quincy, we went to St. Louis with my mom and sister and went to the zoo."

She said, "NO WAY! Last time we went to the zoo, my nephew managed to stick a baby penguin in his pocket and take it home with him. My sister didn't realize anything had happened until she heard the bathtub water running and went to investigate. That's when she found the baby penguin."

I said, "NO WAY! I guess baby penguins don't squeal like baby pigs."

"Nope, they are very quiet. Who knew?"

"Not me."

"I only live here part time," she said. "When it gets too hot, we go back to St. Louis. You know, where they speak English."

"*Claro*," I said.

"What?"

"Nothing. Is this the place?"

"Yes, pull in here to my humble abode."

Her humble abode cost more for one month than my Mexican wife's family spent on food in a year. But there was a swimming pool nobody used; that was the important thing.

She went inside and got her spare keys and I took her back to Costco. When we got back, her friend was holding the original keys. They had somehow fallen to that shadow-spot behind the front tire. A Mexican man had helped her find them.

"And this day started so good," she said.

"Sorry," I said.

"It's not your fault," she said.

That was nice of her to admit.

"I suppose you want MONEY now," she said to me, grumbling with her pocketbook. "18 bucks! This is highway robbery, you know."

"Sorry," I said.

As they got into their car, I heard her say, "God damn, mama needs a margarita!"

EL PENDEJO

I had an American guy in my cab the other day. He was pushing 60 and had a face like an alcoholic attorney. As I was transporting him, my wife, who is Mexican, called me on the phone.

"*Hola guapa*," I said.

We talked for a minute.

When I hung up, the guy said, "You call your wife '*guapa*?'"

"Yes."

"Well," he said, "I speak Spanish fluently and that is not a very nice thing to say to your wife."

"'*Guapa*' means pretty," I said.

"'*Bonita*' means pretty," he said. "'*Guapa*' means slutty, like something you'd say to a street whore. Your wife should be insulted."

"It's strange," I said. "She's not."

"Well, she should be."

"What do you call your wife?" I said.

"I'm divorced," he said. "Haven't talked to the bitch in 14 years."

BATMAN

The new cab driver arrives in the morning wearing all black clothing and a utility belt with a bunch of gadgets hanging off it, the most conspicuous item being a pair of handcuffs. It's early when we all get our cabs and still dark and we use little flashlights to inspect them for damage before driving out of the yard. The new guy takes his flashlight off his utility belt and straps it on his head like a cave-miner. He also has a knife, a pen, phone, a can of mace, a Taser, and other things we haven't been able to identify. Everyone calls him Batman. And nobody gets too close.

PLASMA

A pigeon pecked at his left ear and woke him up. He was lying in the city park where he'd slept all night. He shooed the pigeon away. "Little fucker," he said.

It was dawn and he slowly got up, got his things together in his small green bag, and walked to the plasma bank as the sun was rising. He was tall and thin, with raggedy clothes. His name was Anthony Moore.

By the time he arrived at the plasma bank, a line had already formed outside the door, though the place wouldn't open for another hour. It was summer in Tucson and already 82 degrees.

The people in line, all men, all a bit cracked, knew each other. They were regulars. The loudest talker leaned against the plasma bank door.

"I like to get here early," the loud talker said. "I get up early anyway, and there's no particular point in staying home."

A nod of agreement meandered among them, somnambulists in the building's shade.

"I don't sleep," he said. "I just don't sleep."

One tooth was missing in the middle of his sticky, praline mouth. He had a black shirt tucked into a pair of black jeans. On his leather belt hung a small knife, a pager, two cell phones, and a tape measure. Dark sunglasses and a blue-brimmed cap pulled low. He was well-versed in a variety of subjects, from nano-probe technology to crème brulee.

An enclave of bums staggered by, walking so close together as to be holding each other up. The boniest of all struggled to push a grocery cart, pregnant with bulging, ready-to-burst bags of aluminum cans. The morning sun caused the whole thing to explode with sparkles, like a jeweled tumor.

The bums stopped and one of them leaned into the garbage can. Garbage flew out like a fountain onto the ground all around, onto the sidewalk and street, and every once in a while, his hand would emerge with a bit of some abandoned eatable, or an aluminum can, and relay it to one of the others.

Anthony and the others watched the cop car pull up.

The one with his head in the can came out. His mustache was white from the last of someone's tossed latte.

The cops scolded the bums. One of the bums, the matron, crab-stepped around in circles, picking up all the trash and throwing it back into the can. The cops cocked their heads like robots, bored and cruel with protocol.

The metal gate that protected the front door of the plasma bank was opened ten minutes late.

"Grace is running late again."

"No, it's Thursday."

"Monica, then."

They single-filed in, blinking in the gag-clean air, everything white as an egg, cold as a meat locker. A pecan-skinned Hispanic girl in a white frock gave everybody a little silver bag of juice to drink while we waited.

"Morning, Monica."

"Morning, morning..."

It was nice of her.

They committed their names to the paper on the clipboard on the counter and turned to negotiate the grid of blue plastic chairs. When they each found a suitable spot, they sat down to their juices, as if they were exhausted.

A television was mounted in the upper corner of the room, a bird cage from which squawked the dippy hosts of a morning show. The hosting duo consisted of a taffy-handsome, effeminately enthusiastic, mid-aged male, and a slightly-thickened Puritan female, erect as a fence post, with a mouth like a rubber band that tried to talk intelligently, but always snapped back into an automatic, moronic, hominy-toothed smile.

A white-frocked girl with parboiled hands gripped the clipboard.

"Anthony Moore?" she called.

Anthony got up from his chair. He stood up and walked over toward the girl who was calling his name. She was plain-looking, smooth skin, faint purply smudges beneath her coffee eyes. She took his mugshot and instructed him to go sit down next to another woman in another white smock.

All the employees looked so bored, so resigned, like old circus animals.

Anthony sat down in front of the other lady.

"Give me your finger," she said. She pricked him with her little pricker, the bitch, then milked the scarlet blood out into a tiny tube. The machine did the rest. Machines did everything, everything important. The humans served to fill in the blanks, to act as connectors. He hated to see people who have been doing a job so long they have become like a machine. He had been a machine for years and years.

"We have to check your blood for proteins," the woman said, not looking in his eyes, "and make sure you're not diabetic."

She stared at the computer screen, immersed in what she saw. Never had she seen anything like this. The screen was swiveled so he couldn't read it, but a red hazard light blinked on and off. He could see it reflected in her eyes, which were screwed up until her muddy black eyeliner cracked. Her mouth moved in a silent series of puckers, lip-chews, and clucks.

No trouble, please no trouble.

His hands were clammy as frogs' butts. The air in the building maintained a steady 64 degrees, to keep the germs down, to keep the blood from spoiling. He didn't see a single fly, in fact, while he waited for the truth.

Finally, she stopped looking at the screen and wrote something down.

"Well?" he said.

"Looks good," she said. Just like that.

143

Then there was another wait, another corner, another set of chairs, this time red chairs.

"Anthony?" the doctor said.

He was short and a fitness addict. There was not enough fat on his body to fill a blood vial. His musculature was that of a triathlete on heroin. There was black stubble on his suntanned arms where he had shaved them. His black hair was parted over his left eye, with each hair combed back on either side, where they remained, obedient as Mormon wives. His whole head looked like a wood carving.

He knocked Anthony's knees with a rubber hammer, listened to his heart with his safe-cracker stethoscope, probed his stomach and kidneys, waiting for him to yelp.

He kept writing things down without saying a word.

"Everything okay?" Anthony said.

"Fine, fine," the doctor said. "Most of the major tests will take a week to come back, so I can't say much until then."

"Oh," Anthony said. "I can still give plasma today, right?"

"Yes," the doctor said. "If you're sick, we'll contact you, and your plasma will be destroyed."

He wrote something down, then stopped. "The tests take a week, and if we find something like AIDS, we send it in for a secondary test, which takes another week."

"Two weeks."

"I made the mistake of telling a guy once, last year, that he had AIDS," the doctor said, "and then the secondary tests came back and it turned out he really didn't have it. I felt terrible. I drove over to his address as soon as I found out, but he wasn't there. He'd already moved."

"Oh, boy."

"He moved the day after I told him."

"Ever find him?"

He shook his head no. Then he seemed to snap back and remembered where he was.

"No tattoos?" he said, his pen poised.

"No."

"Nothing?"

"Nothing."

"Not even a dot?"

"A dot?"

They looked at each other.

"Have you had sex with a prostitute within the last year?" the doctor said.

"No."

"Have you been incarcerated within the last 72 hours?"

"No."

Then Anthony got to pee into a cup.

"How much you want?" he said to the doctor as he took the cup.

"Anything," he shrugged.

When Anthony was done, the doctor snapped on a rubber glove, and the piss was analyzed in about ten seconds. He walked back over to the desk, signed one more form, and then sent him to wait in another place.

"Everything okay?" Anthony said.

"Just one thing," the doctor said. "Your crits are a little high."

"My what?"

"Your crits. Tell the nurse they were a little high. She'll know."

"Is that bad?"

"99 percent of the time, no."

"But I should tell the nurse?"

"Tell the nurse and she can keep an eye on it," the doctor said.

"Crits a little high," Anthony said. "Got it."

The chairs in the next room were yellow.

"Anthony?" the lady said. Another clipboard crier. They all wore white smocks, like snow people, snow-royalty. It was colder in each room. She flattened her clipboard against her chest and looked at him. He stood up.

"My crits are a little high," he said.

"How high?" she said.

"He didn't say, just a little high, he said to tell you and you'd know."

"Okay," she said.

"Is that bad?"

"No problem."

He followed her into the main room. He had passed a high-security clearance test and was finally allowed to see the nerve center. It was like the inside of an alien spaceship, with human specimens prone on large gray recliners, looking drugged and hauntingly mollified. The lady led Anthony to a futuristic recliner. It was gray and heavily padded like the others and curved like a fallen S. He climbed on, happy to relax. It was the most comfortable chair he'd sat in in years.

The recliners were set along the walls of the room, facing one another. He looked at the people. Everybody kept gripping their fists, gripping and gripping.

"First time, eh?" the nurse said to Anthony as he lay there. She looked like a trucker's wife, with a deep voice, a twisted nose, and strong shoulders.

"You just lie right here, there's nothin' to it," she said. She walked around, attending to others. Then she swung back to Anthony's bed/chair.

"Just relax," she said. "I'm not gonna stick you yet; Marcela will do that. Which arm do you want to use? Doesn't matter?"

She wrote something on his chart, tossed it on top of the machine. "Okay," she said. "See those lights there?" She indicated the machine to his right. "You want them to be green. Except when they're red."

"Green, except when they're red."

"Right," she said. "When they're red, don't worry about it. But when they're green, you pump your hand, keep pumping and pumping, okay?"

"Keep pumping."

"Make sure they stay green, all of them, not two or of them, all four."

"What about my crits?"

"You just let me worry about your crits."

She walked over and unhooked a bottle from another person's machine. She wrote something with a black marker on the bottle and, without looking at Anthony, she kept talking.

"This is what your plasma looks like," she said. "Looks like apple juice." She walked the bottle over to a man who took it away behind a wall. She walked back over to me and slapped Anthony's machine the way a mechanic would slap the hood of a car. "Your blood goes in here, is separated into plasma here, and then drips down through this, and into this bottle."

He looked at the empty bottle.

"She'll make some noise," she said, "but don't worry about it. A few beeps and hums means she's working right."

That machine was like a combination of R2-D2 and Dracula.

"And when you hear her make the charge call," the nurse said, "Doot-doodooDOOO! That means you're done. Any questions?"

He shook his head no.

"Okay, then." She clapped her hands. "Marcela!" She rushed off and a girl the size of a professional wrestler went over. She looked at Anthony's chart and prepared her sadistic works.

"My crits are high."

"I know," she said.

She knew.

The thought of a needle can send people into a panic. It's as if you can feel that needle going all the way up through your arm and past your elbow and shoulder and into your heart and then even lower. Anthony knew a boy who jumped into the lake, feet first, and landed on a sharp, broken tree trunk, submerged below the water, which pierced his heel and traveled up his leg like a large splinter, all the way to his hip. Needles: nothing should be that sharp.

Marcela busied herself with her clamps and hoses and scissors, her tongue hanging out the side of her mouth, like she was hot-wiring it. She applied iodine with a Q-tip, which was the color of grasshopper spit, in slowly widening circles onto the soft belly of Anthony's thin right arm.

The scary part about needles is by the time you feel them, they're already in you. Bullets are the same way, but much worse; Anthony knew that. Even if you watch it happening, it's like watching a baseball player swing the bat while sitting in the nosebleed seats: you hear the crack a second later, and your senses seem to be lying to you.

Anthony gripped his hand.

There was a guy to his left. His machine was obstructing his face. All Anthony could see was his body, from the chest down, lying on his recliner. He wore jeans and basketball shoes. He sounded young.

"First time?" the faceless guy said.

"Yep."

"Just keep gripping," he said.

Anthony gripped extra hard on account of his high crits. His fingernails dug into his palm.

The faceless guy flirted with the snow-royalty nurses as they went around.

"Yolanda," the faceless guy said, "I'm not talking to you today."

"Why not?" Yolanda flipped her long black hair while administering to someone else.

"You blew me off last Friday, that's why not," he said. "We were supposed to go for drinks. What happened to drinks?"

"I told you I had plans," Yolanda said. "Besides, what would your girlfriend think?"

"She wouldn't care."

"Ah hah."

Another girl walked by.

"When are we gonna go out and do something, Paula?" the faceless guy said to her.

"I'm Erika," the girl said.

"Erika, right, that's what I said," he said. "How about tonight? Let's go out, you and me."

"Are you gonna spend all your plasma money on little ol' me?" Erika said.

"Hey, I got lots of money, babe," the faceless guy said. "I just do this to help the kids." He gestured to a poster on the wall with a big, smiling child supposed to have been saved by somebody's plasma.

When the plasma bottle was full, a saline solution would be pushed through the tube into Anthony's bloodstream.

"Just wait," the faceless guy said to him. "When that saline hits your blood, it's cold, man. I shivered the first time it happened. But now, hell, now I love it, it's great."

His bottle of plasma was almost full. He was ready for the saline.

"I'm almost done," he said. "Here it comes!"

Just a couple more drops to go.

"Here she comes, baby!"

It did look like apple juice.

Across the room lay a fifty-something year old man with bags under his eyes. He kept falling asleep. The nurses would smack his leg as they walked by.

"WAKE UP, EVERYBODY!" they would shout.

Directly adjacent to Anthony was a young, maybe 20-year-old guy, pickled and porky, with rosy cheeks and retarded eyes. His feet stood up at the end of his recliner like clown's feet, huge and peanut-shaped. Everybody was in this same position with slightly elevated feet, a disarming position. Everybody was on the same level: the bottom.

An hour later, Anthony's plasma bottle was almost full. A good-looking nurse had just come on shift. Red hair piled upon a tiny head, not a single pore in her opal face, smart glasses that didn't rest too high on her nose. She wore the same white smock that the rest of them had, but somehow hers was alluring.

"You're almost done," she said to him.

"Already?" he said.

The machine did its pathetic little *"doot-doodooDOO!"* The saline solution poured through the tube. It rushed like peppermint through Anthony's veins. His whole right arm went numb, like menthol oil rubbed underneath the skin, directly on the raw muscle.

The cutie disconnected him. She put a piece of cotton on the tiny bite in his arm.

"Hold this here," she said. Their fingers touched. *How long had it been since that happened,* he wondered. She wrapped him up and patted his shoulder.

"Good job," she said. Then she handed him a white ticket.

"I don't know how," he said, looking at the ticket. "I've never done this before."

"Come on," she said, "I'll show you."

She walked him over to another machine. He wanted her to hold his hand.

"You put the number from your ticket in there," she said. "Then you read the directions here." Her arm and perfect little hand reached across his body to point at a sign on the machine. The sign instructed users in the proper method of entering your birth date on the keypad, which was the next step. He was too engrossed in her hand to read the sign, and so the first time he tried it, he did it wrong.

"Oops," he said. "What?"

"Hit clear," she sighed impatiently.

Finally, after three attempts, the $20 bill slid out. He turned to smile at her, but she was gone.

He walked out the door and into the bright day. It felt good to be walking in the sun with a $20 bill in his pocket. He breathed deep. An easy spirit flowed through him. He walked up Cherry Street and took a left on 22nd toward the outlet bakery.

THE JUMPING-OFF PLACE

James was short and skinny, with a peninsula of purple eczema running along his right forearm. He had gray stubble on his chin and eyes, which crossed once in a while. His diet consisted of fried chicken, hamburgers, and cheese pizza. He had some kind of digestive disease, arthritis, fibromyalgia, diabetes, and a bad back. Also, he was also manic-depressive. And he got migraines.

He lived with his mother and her 11 cats. Driving a taxi got him out of the house.

One hot Saturday morning, he was sitting in his taxi in the parking lot of Walmart. The cab's two-way radio blurted to life.

"Cab 232?" the female dispatcher said through static.

He grabbed the radio microphone and it seemed to jump from his hand like a fish. It landed on the floor. He lifted his right foot and the long curly black cord got tangled around his ankle. Leaning over, his face pressed into the steering wheel as he blindly unwound the cord. In the awkward position, his calf cramped and he moaned as he sat up and reeled in the microphone, hand over hand.

"232 here, James here," he wheezed through yellow teeth.

"232, how ya doing today?"

"Purty good."

She laughed. "Okay, go to the Hampton on Oracle. A woman named Sara. She's going you-know-where."

There was only one reason why a cab driver would be sent to the

Hampton on Oracle: to pick up a passenger and take them to Cottonwood. Cottonwood is a drug rehabilitation center out near the Saguaro National Park, in the middle of the desert, and the Hampton Inn on Oracle Road is, so to speak, the jumping-off place for many visitors on their way to Cottonwood because it is the closest swanky hotel. Cottonwood has a minor fee of $5,000 a month and includes massages, mud baths, acupuncture, chef-prepared meals, and horseback riding.

James pulled his taxi up to the front doors of the Hampton. He didn't see anybody, so he got out to wait. He lit a cigarette and leaned against his cab. While he was smoking, a woman came out and looked at him. She had a bag around her shoulder and pulled another bag on wheels. She wore a long green dress, which was sexy and expensive-looking. Her black hair fell in her face and her eyes were tired and red.

"Are you my taxi?" she said in a British accent.

"Are you Sara?" James said. He threw his cigarette down on the ground.

"Oh, no," she said.

"You're not Sara?" he said, bending down to retrieve his smoke.

"Oh, I'm Sara," she said.

He stood up quickly and again threw the cigarette away.

"Can I take your bag?" he said.

"I can't ride with you," she said, standing straight and firm in the walkway.

"Why not?"

"The cigarette smoke," she said. "I'll smell it on you all the way there."

"Uh…" he said.

"How far is it from here, this…this place I'm going?"

"It's a long ways," he said, pointing out into the desert west of town.

"No, I can't ride with you," she said, looking off toward where he pointed. "The smoke is in your shirt; I'll smell it all the way there, I'm allergic."

"What do you want me to do?" he said. "You want me to take my shirt

152

off?" He laughed.

A confused look came over her face. She cocked her head and looked at his skinny frame. He was a nervous little rat of a man.

"Well," she said, thinking. "I suppose that would...yes, okay, that'll do."

"You mean...?" James said. He didn't want to lose the fare. It was a 30-minute drive to Cottonwood; 45 bucks at least. "All right," he shrugged. He took off his shirt and stood under the roof of the entryway to the hotel. The weather was fine and hot. He grinned at her, but she didn't smile. He bent his ribbed body over and stuffed his shirt under his driver's seat.

"Don't put it down there," Sara said. "I'll smell it from there."

James looked at her. She was full of designer pills. James was full of pills, too. He was on blood pressure pills, pills to go to sleep, pills to wake up, pills before he ate, pills after he ate, pills for depression, pills for aggression, pills for pain. He also smoked marijuana each morning and drank a 12-pack of highly caffeinated soft drinks every day.

He walked around and put his shirt in the trunk, making a display of showing her. She nodded. Then he shut the trunk and got in the cab.

She leaned over and stuck her nose into the back seat. She clutched her bag to her breast and her nostrils twitched. She looked around at the torn brown seat, the empty pack of gum in the crease, footprints from the recent rain on the grimy floor mats.

"Lovely," she said with that sarcastic British accent.

She looked at the hotel doors one last time and finally got in and closed the door.

James inched up to the edge of Oracle Road and stopped, looking to all the world like a nudist, and activated his right blinker. It ticked like a clock as the traffic flew by. Oracle Road was fast and busy and the trucks created a wind that rocked them. He finally eased out and made a couple of successful lane changes. Sara looked out the window at the summer day.

"So, what's your name?" she said after a few minutes.

"James."

"I'm Sara," she said. "But you know that."

"He he, yeah."

"You ever been to the Grand Canyon, James?"

"Nope."

"How long have you lived in Arizona?"

"All my life."

"What are you, about 45?" she said.

"33," he said.

"Oh," she said. "I figured as long as I was coming all this goddamned way across the goddamned world, I might as well see the Grand Canyon."

"You're from England?"

"How'd you guess?" she said.

He looked at her in the rearview mirror. She avoided his eyes.

"So, how was it?"

"It was outstanding," Sara said. "I cried. I really did. I stood there on the edge of that great big hole in the earth and cried like a baby. It was a real catharsis."

"I've heard that," James said, even though he had no idea what "catharsis" meant.

"Everyone should see the Grand Canyon before they die," she said.

Her eyes got redder and bugged out a little bit and she began to cry again, quietly. She rolled down the window halfway and smelled the desert air.

"I'm sorry," she said.

"Don't worry about it."

"Do you mind so much if we just not talk, James?" she said. "Would that be all right?"

"Of course, Sara."

25 minutes later, James turned his taxi right onto Cottonwood Drive and followed it for two curving miles until he came to a security gate with a little building next to it. The Cottonwood trees were shedding like crematory ash.

A neckless flunky in a blue uniform poked his head out his window and looked down at James.

"Where's your shirt?"

"It's in the trunk."

"Why?"

"I can explain everything, officer!" Sara said loudly from the back seat. "I asked him to do it; no problem, my name is Sara Worthington, I should be on the list."

He scowled, hesitated, and looked at a clipboard.

"Okay, Miss Worthington," he said. Then he turned to James. "Just drop her off and get out of here."

The 12-foot tall wrought iron gates opened slowly and James eased his taxi through. It was like entering a different world, a heavenly world: acres of deep green, shoe-swallowing grass, scrupulous landscaping, lavish Spanish Colonial Revival architecture, flowers, and fish ponds. There was a *feng shui* lyricism to the layout of the little bungalows, gurgling fountains, walkways, benches, cactus, acutely raked rock gardens, rapturous sculpture, lapping palms, old, gnarly mesquites, fairyland palo verdes, and of course, the dry-weeping cottonwoods. Marmalade melodies filled the air from a three-piece band set up on an adorable knoll. The pastel green of tennis courts flashed to the left. People walked and milled around in their country club whites and $200 hats, most of them smiling and laughing like a family reunion.

James eased the cab halfway around a vast circular drive and stopped along the curbing.

"Here we are," James said.

"What do I owe you?" Sara said.

"$49.50."

"$49.50?" she said. "Highway robbery!"

"Make it 49 even," he said.

"Jesus Christ," she said, digging into her designer bag.

"Here's a 50."

She looked at the bill as she handed it to him.

"Your money is so ugly," she said.

James took it.

"Keep the change," she said. Her tone was insinuating, as if she expected that favor returned to her someday.

She yanked her bag out and stood there in the sun, straightening herself.

"Good luck!" he said.

He slowly pulled away, circling the gigantic roundabout. He passed the guardhouse and waved to the guard, who scowled again. He thought about putting his shirt back on, but he liked the feel of his bare back on the seat and the air on his chest with the window down. Out on the desert highway, he lit a cigarette, thinking about the Grand Canyon. He decided he should go and see it someday.

NOVEMBER IN JULY

It was 11am on July 3rd, the middle of the monsoon season. I was sweating in my taxi when I was dispatched to a nightclub named November. A poor neighborhood of trailers and railroad tracks and seedy corner stores and a snarling pit bull in every stinking chain-linked yard. The sign: "NOVEMBER BAR AND CABARET."

I splashed my cab through the pothole puddles in the parking lot and stopped. I got out and walked up to the heavy front door, opened it.

"TAXI!" I yelled into the moist smoky darkness. "TAXI FOR ED!"

My eyes adjusted. The bartender was a big female Filipino frog with murder in her ribbit. A giant horseshoe bar charred in black cherry light. Light fixtures in the shape of breasts poked out of the ceiling. Six or eight men hunched around the sloppy gargoyle bar. Shadowy booths along two walls, cubby holes in an opium den. On the far side of the room, there was a small, circular stage about three inches high where a woman danced naked around a flimsy pole. She was at least 50 years old and looked to have formerly been a man.

The old white man who was Ed arduously lifted himself with his hands from his stool at the bar and stood up. He turned and approached me, where I wavered at the door like an apparition.

I drove him to an address up the street. He didn't say a word the entire time. Maybe he was too drunk. Or maybe he was just stupid. He swayed with the turns and burped and frowned at the dark clouds, which were still bright compared to the bar.

The fare was $15.25. The old man dug a 20 out of an ancient wallet, handed it to me. Then he got out slowly and stumbled into a trailer in a dilapidated court called Twin Palms. A naked baby sat on the floorboards of the porch of the trailer next to Ed's. The baby was alone and it stared at me as I drove off. *It kind of looked like me,* I thought. He had his mouth open like he wanted to throw a fit but didn't quite have the energy to begin.

THE DOUBLE

132 West Jacinto, Apartment 6

I pull my cab up to 132 W. Jacinto and park. Rosalita Morales is 23 years old. She has big, lumpy formations on her left arm where they have inserted needles and tubes for her kidney dialysis three times a week, for years and years and years.

"Morning," I say as she climbs in the cab. She has dark skin and eyes, skinny.

"Yes, I guess it is, isn't it?" she says.

I take her to a doctor on the east side, which is different than her usual place: the dialysis center. She is inside the doctor's office for only about 30 minutes. I wait for her in the cab.

When Rosalita comes out, she's crying.

"Oh, shit, shit," she says in the cab when we were on our way back to her apartment.

"Bad news?"

"You see this?" she says, referring to the lumpy formations on her left arm, on the opposite side of the elbow. "That fucking doctor says there's clotting going on in my arm and we have to use the *other* arm! That's all I fucking need."

She looks at her right arm, her good arm. It is smooth and thin, beautiful. She strokes it a couple of times and then looks at the ruined cauliflower of her left arm.

"Either my right arm or one of my legs," she says. "Those are my

159

choices. I'm gonna look like more of a freak than I do already!"

"You're on the organ list, right?"

"Yes, but I just got on that list not too long ago."

"But you've been on dialysis for years."

"Three years ago, when I was 18, my mother gave me one of her kidneys. You can live with only one."

"Yes."

I turn left on Congress, right by the statue of Poncho Villa on his horse. The horse is rearing with its two front feet in the air and a fierce look on its face, which mirrors the look on Poncho Villa's face.

"Well, three months into it, everything was going fucking great! Then I stopped taking my anti-rejection drugs."

"Why?"

"I don't know, I really don't know, but my body rejected the...my mom's...kidney."

"That's rough."

"So, it was kinda my fault."

"Yes."

"I was in the hospital for three months, I almost didn't make it. So, now I'm on the list again, but they didn't want to put me on it for a long time, because of all that, but they finally did anyway. I had to go through like a million fucking psych tests. My mom was real mad at me."

I take a left at Grant Road and miss the yellow arrow just barely. I feel the camera flash through my windshield and know the automatic cameras have caught me running the light. The ticket will appear in the company's mailbox within ten business days. I will get the ticket and a lecture and will have to pay $134 to the courts. I've already had two others. One more and I'm gone.

"My brother said he would give me one of his kidneys," Rosalita says. "But he's skeptical. I can't blame him."

I pull up to her apartment and she climbs out.

"Thank you so much," she says.

Her face is as sad as an old heavy sunflower, dried seeds falling to the ground like teeth.

Corner of 36th and Country Club

I know I shouldn't stop the cab, I should just keep on driving, but I need the cash. The neighborhood is shitty but it's still early, only 10 o'clock in the morning. Two guys are standing at the corner where the mini-mart is, waving at me. Two young Latino-looking males, dressed in price-tag-still-on baggy pants and big, long shirts. The police don't need to profile; people profile themselves by being so needy for approval. They can't resist looking the part.

I stop the cab. They get in the back of the cab before I really know what's going on.

"12th and Valencia," one of them says.

They both scrunch way down in the seats.

"I'm gonna need the money up front," I say. "That's a long way."

"Just drive."

"Not without the cash, man."

He opens his wallet and flashes it at me. It's loaded with bills. Then he puts it away again.

"I need the money in my hand. 30 bucks."

"I ain't giving you shit, man," he says, and gives the other guy a fancy handshake. They both laugh.

"Then you're not going anywhere, get out."

They look at me with a hatred that seems far greater than is warranted. The quiet one jumps out and starts walking off. From the way he walks, it is clear he's drunk. The other one just sits there.

"Get out."

Finally, he sits up and opens his door and slowly puts one foot down on the pavement. Then, as I turn back towards the front, he leans into the cab again and swings his left hand over the seat and hits me on the right side of his face. It stings, swells up immediately. My pride is shattered, and I'm dizzy for a few moments. The kid laughs and struts slowly off to his friend. I drive out of there feeling very lucky, and unlucky, at the same

161

time.

2550 North Oracle, Apartment 6755

Some of these apartment complexes are as big as villages and as confusing as LSD labyrinths. It's a medical voucher, Charlotte Bercher. Her apartment is 4512. After 15 minutes, I find the right building and then begin looking for the apartment. There she is waving at me, walking down the sidewalk. Middle-aged white lady, like a sun-bleached eggplant.

"How you doing today?" I say.

"Oh, not so good. It's getting hot, isn't it? I almost fainted."

"Yes, very hot here in the summertime."

"I wish my neighbor would give me the money he owes me," she says. "He owes me five dollars. I've got to do laundry. The office has a machine and you put the money in the machine and it puts the money on this card and you use the card on the washers and driers."

"Ah."

"I don't have any money on my card now. All I could do was wash my towels, I couldn't dry them."

"Why don't you hang your towels out to dry in the sun?"

She looks horrified at the idea and gives a scoff. "Ha! I mean, I'm not prejudiced or anything, you know, but, the, er, the *Mexicans* are always doing that, hanging their clothes out like that."

"Makes sense to me," I say. "It's free, it's natural."

Charlotte receives a government check every month and her basic needs are taken care of. She is safe and secure as a hamster in a Coca-Cola cup.

"I don't like scratchy towels," she says.

"And that's your right."

"Towels get all scratchy if you dry them in the sun."

"Yuck."

"Oh, yes," she says. "Plus, driers are faster."

Her days are narcotic run-ons of soap operas, rape fantasies, grilled cheese sandwiches, and country music. Every once in a while, she gets

162

lucky and has a doctor's appointment.

"Do you know I signed up for the George Straight fan club?"

"No, I didn't."

"But that bastard never sent me anything, not even a hello."

"People are rude these days."

"Hmmmph."

She has a 12 o'clock appointment. Colon exploratory probe.

"I haven't eaten since yesterday," she says. "When you take me home later, can we stop at We Went Wongs?"

"Maybe."

"I'll buy you a Coke."

"Okay."

I drop her off and head out. I take a big drink of water from a bottle that was frozen in my freezer all night, and now thawing slowly. It's as cold as glacial run-off on my lips and throat.

1280 South Vista Del Monte

I decide to work a double shift, so when the sun goes down, I'm still out here. The night goes slow for a while. Then about midnight, I get caught in a gun fight outside a frat party. Some gang members invade the place. A couple of college girls jump in my cab. They are not the girls who called me to come get them, but I don't care and I get out of there with some bullets zinging. It's confusing and scary and the girls are crying and cussing and one of them is very drunk.

When I get them to their sorority house, the drunk one opens her door and does a face-plant on the sidewalk. She is complete dead weight. Me and the other girl lift her up and drag her to the front door of the sorority house. The passed-out girl is wearing a dress and the dress rises up to her waist. She has yellow thong panties and orange, waxed legs.

The fare is $14.50. The girl is annoyed when I ask for money. She gets a 20 out of her $200 purse.

"Just give me back a five," she says.

I keep the 50 cents and save it for the future.

163

The Pearl Nightclub, Oracle and Whitmore

A drunk guy drops a $100 bill on the floor of the cab when he gets in. I reach down and gather the bill up in my fingers as the drunk guy turns to look at a woman who walks out the door of the nightclub.

281 West Laguna

It's almost 6 o'clock and I've worked for 24 hours straight, which is technically against the rules, but there are ways around the rules. Just when I'm about to go home, I get another call for a nearby address. One more, why not. I drive over. A young white kid comes out of the house dressed in what looks like a restaurant uniform. It's early, but the sun is well up.

"The Furr's restaurant on Saint Mary's," the kid says.

Furr's is a local family restaurant. I head west on Saint Mary's Road.

"Going to work, eh?" I say. I figure the kid's a breakfast waiter at Furr's.

"Yep," the kid says.

Tucson is waking up, but I am drowsy and nearly done. How many years of this? How many years more of it do I have, can I take? I'm 47 now, been doing this for 14, have no plan for retirement, haven't paid taxes for a long time. Dues, yes, but taxes, no.

When they get to the Furr's restaurant, the meter says $20.85. I turn around to tell the kid the amount and the kid is already out of the cab.

"I gotta get the money from inside," the kid says.

He goes inside the restaurant, which looks empty.

"Shit!"

I jump out and run after him. I open the door and goes inside. A couple of waiters are standing behind the counter; another is setting the tables. There is the sound of a vacuum cleaner and it smells like potatoes and onions frying.

"Did you guys see a kid come through here?"

They both nod and point to the other door on the other side of the lobby that leads outside.

"He doesn't work here?" I ask.

"We've never seen him before," one of the waiters says.

164

I run to the other door and go outside into the early morning. I see him now, way down the block, running. I can't catch him and really, I wouldn't want to find out what would happen if I did catch him. I stand there and watch him run. Go, man, go.

I'm breathing heavy, but it slowly goes back to normal. I know I won't be able to sleep now and I don't feel like going home. I go back inside the restaurant and sit down in a corner booth and look at the menu. I'm the first customer of the day.

THE ROAD TO THE CASINO DEL SOL

Four Buddhists, dressed in orange robes, fold themselves into my cab outside the colossal brass doors of La Paloma, a lavish resort on the north side of Tucson. They're Asian, one man in his fifties, and two men and a young woman in their thirties, all bald-headed and with flawless complexions. One of the younger men has eyeglasses. The woman scrunches in between the younger men in the back seat. The older man perches himself shotgun.

"You take us to casino?" he says to me. There is a photo of me pasted to the dashboard, fat and tired-looking, with the name Matt Glasford, independent contractor, written under it.

My eyes lit up. The casino is on the Tohono O'odham Indian reservation out in the desert, at least 40 minutes away. It was a jackpot fare: 80 bucks.

"The Casino Del Sol, yes sir," I say, and punch the meter.

"This is good casino?" the old Asian man says.

"Oh, they'll take your money."

"I wear red fo' luck," he says, showing Jesus a bright red pin of some kind on his orange robe.

"You'll need it."

"Yes."

"Where ya from?" I say. "China?"

"Japan," the old man says, frowning.

"Sorry."

167

It's 5 o'clock in the evening and we're driving directly into the sunset. The traffic is Friday rush hour; even the nuns from St. Elizabeth's will cut you off and not repent a bit. It's roasting hot outside. The windows of the cab are up and the air conditioning is flowing.

I have no religion, but there seems to be something special about today. It's a quiet ride. The sinking sun leaks pink and purple and orange in front of us. The old man doesn't notice because he has nodded off. His head is lowered onto his breastbone. I think he is meditating until he begins to snore. Then I check the rearview mirror: one of the younger men is also asleep. His head has fallen back and his mouth is open and his eyeglasses are tilting into the milky pond of his cheek.

Five minutes of lotus-smooth highway later, the other man is asleep too.

I look at the woman in the rearview mirror. I imagine my thought is a butterfly that flies out of his forehead and lands on her nose. She looks out the window at the desert that begins at the outskirts of the city. The red rocky hills are spiked with cactus and cholla and creosote, nothing kind there, nothing soft. She won't meet my eyes. She seems unhappy, like she is involved in some kind of tremendous mistake.

"Looks like it's just you and me," I break the silence, talking to the young woman. It feels like the two of us are the only ones there, because we are the only ones awake. She doesn't say anything. She doesn't smile. She looks at me with puffy, raindrop eyes. But the old man jerks awake. He sits straight up and blinks a couple times.

"We they yet?" he says.

"Another 20 minutes."

He grunts. 30 seconds later, he's asleep again.

I always get a feeling when people fall asleep in my cab. They trust me to get them safely to where they want to go. Buddhists are trusting souls, aren't they? In either case, I am relieved when we arrive at the casino. I feel my blood pressure lowering with the promise of solitude.

The Japanese Buddhists climb out of the cab, stretch toward the sky. The old man reaches inside his robe and comes out with a wallet. He pays me. The woman flashes me a look and then turns away. They shuffle off toward the door of the casino.

I drive away, back to the city.

So are the separations of this world.

THE STANDARD

It was mid-day and hot as usual in Tucson, the sun hanging there like an angry fundamentalist. Five sorority girls left their dorm building and walked down the smoldering sidewalk in flip-flops and pastel dresses. Gadabout bimbos with low-swung hips and lazy postures ambling along as if it was an almost unbearable burden to be so desirable. I was sitting in my taxi looking at them.

"Can you take us to the Standard?" squeaked one of the mall bunnies.

"Love to," I said. The Standard was one of the many off-campus housing complexes for the wealthy college kids from California and Boston and New York. This was the University of Arizona, gathering place for mega-maniacal meat.

They all wore bathing suits underneath their pastel dresses.

"Pool party at the Standard?" I said.

They looked at me like I was a pervert, or an idiot, or both. I was way too old to matter.

"Oh, yea-ah, poo-el party, dude," one of them finally said.

Once a month, one of the off-campus apartment buildings hosted huge, hideous swimming pool parties. Hundreds of braindead uni-kids packed the shimmering green pool shoulder to shoulder, each one pouring beer into his/her mouth above the water and draining it out below. They were like giant petri dishes of percolating hormones, desperate posturing, and piss.

There were so many girls in the group that one of them was forced to sit in the front seat of the cab. This great distance between her and her

171

herd made her nervous. She smelled a leopard on the air. She kept turning around. In the span of a 15-minute drive, she could find herself cut off from her bitchy friends, and this meant the world to her; she had no concept of survival without them. She pulled down the visor and looked at herself in the mirror. Then she pulled out a mirror from her purse and looked in that. Finally, she rolled down the window and looked at herself in the side mirror outside the cab. The others complained about the hot wind that came in and messed their hair, and the girl in the front seat rolled the window up again, pouting.

Halfway to the Standard, we came to a place on Stone Avenue where there is a clear view of the mountains to the north.

"What are those mountains?" one of the girls said to me.

"Those are the Catalina Mountains," I said.

"Is Tucson higher than New York?" another girl said.

"You from New York?" I said.

A snicker scattered among them. "Well, ya-uh."

"New York's at sea level," I said. "We're at about 2,200 feet here."

They had no idea what I was talking about.

"Yes," I said, "it's higher here."

There was a murmur of understanding.

Then another girl said: "Does that mean we weigh less?"

I searched the rearview mirror for a sign of a joke, but realized it was an honest question.

"Yes, you weigh less," I said.

There was a giggle of delight.

"But," I said, "your breasts are smaller, too."

They all looked down at their cleavage and one girl pawed herself protectively.

I pulled up to the entrance of the Standard and was cut off by a young kid in a shiny new SUV that was bigger than my apartment. The kid's beautiful, untroubled face scowled at me.

The girls spilled out of the cab, eager to display their gaudy, orange,

172

plastic bodies for the eye-rape of burger-eating frat boys. They'd never had to work or worry in their lives, and most likely never would. Their parents injected three grand into their bank account every month. They only knew one thing: comfort, the constant, immediate satisfaction of even their smallest wishes. And, honestly, they were not even pretty. There was more beauty and soul and warmth and life in the smallest finger of the poorest Mexican girl working at the tiniest market on the south side of Tucson than these girls had between them.

The fare was 22 bucks and they each wanted to pay for their part separately. Everything else in their lives was done with one collective mind, but when it came to this matter, they insisted on individuality. Each of them had a $20 bill and they wiped out all my change. I thought I might get some of the small bills back in the form of a tip, but no.

After I dropped them off, I went into the nearest mini-mart and bought a candy bar with one of the 20s just to have some change again. The lady behind the cash register told me to have a nice day. I told her I'd try.

THINKING'S GOT NOTHING TO DO WITH IT

It was a cookie cutter neighborhood and nobody answered the phone, so I got out of my cab and walked to the door. I rang the bell. Dogs barked inside.

"Who is it?"

"Taxi!" I said through the door.

"I'll be right out, sir!"

"Okay!"

"Is that Don?" she said.

"No!"

"Oh! I thought it might be Don!"

"It's Matt!"

"Don took me last week!"

"Don sucks Boy Scouts," I mumbled.

"What?"

"Can we get a move on, please?"

14 minutes later, she opened the door. She was in a wheelchair.

"I broke my ankle," she said. "The doctors wanted me to use crutches, but fuck crutches."

She had an emaciated body and terrible acne. She was maybe 30. She had been pretty at one time. She was one of the millions who had given up and blamed the world.

175

"Forgive me, I have no strength," she said, "would you mind?" I steered her down the driveway to the taxi. Then she held her arms out to me like she wanted a hug. I lifted her from the chair into the cab. My face was very close to hers during the lift; her flat breasts pressed into my chest. She smelled like death; death and entitlement. I put the wheelchair in the trunk.

She yapped the whole way to her doctor's: the government stole her kids...her ex-husband beat her...her mother was a bitch...there are strange insects that come in through her vents at night...she used to work with Charles Barkley...

"What's that about the insects?"

"They get in the bed and bite you," she said. "But nobody believes me."

"Why don't you catch one in a jar or something? Then you'll have proof."

"I tried that," she said. "But they disintegrate when they are captured."

"Little bastards," I said.

"I used to have so much fucking money," she said, "I'd leave brand new cars on stranger's driveways. I'd put big yellow bows on the cars and just leave them there. I wouldn't even sign my name."

"You sound like a generous person."

"I'm broke now," she said. "You think you know broke? You don't know shit about it."

"I'm rolling in money, myself."

When we got to the doctor, I got the wheelchair out of the trunk and lifted her into it and wheeled her inside. Her doctor was on the seventh floor, so we went up the elevator.

She was finished in 30 minutes. I went back up the elevator and wheeled her out and down and lifted her back into the taxi and put the chair back in the trunk.

Then she needed to go to the pharmacy. When we got to the pharmacy, she said, "Ah, damn."

"What?"

"I forgot, I changed pharmacies. The girl at this pharmacy is a fucking

176

cow!"

So we went to another pharmacy. I lifted her from the taxi into the chair and wheeled her in.

While she was waiting for her prescription to be filled, she wanted to do a little shopping. I pushed her down the frozen food aisle. She grabbed ice cream sandwiches, popsicles, a frozen cake, and frozen cookie dough. We went through the cashiers and I held her bag. We went back and got her "medicine." Then it was back to the taxi, and more lifting.

Back on the road, she gripped her little rattling bottle.

"It just makes me so sad sometimes," she said. "I hate taking these pills."

There was an ecstatic gleam in her eyes. "I never used to do drugs at all," she said. "I never even drank! And pot? Forget it. I was a clean thing when I was young, I was clean and innocent. But, those doctors, those fucking doctors! And the pain, you know?"

"Yeah," I said, rubbing my forehead. I thought about my last customer, who was 24 years old and got his legs cut off in a car accident when a drunk guy hit him. I drove him to his physical therapy. Despite his condition, it made me smile the way he talked and had sense and perspective and humility and kindness.

"I totaled seven cars last year," she said. "I don't drive anymore."

"Good thinking."

"Thinking's got nothing to do with it; they took my license away."

"Sorry."

"None of those accidents were my fault," she said. "Except that last one. That last one was partially my fault."

"Is that how you broke your ankle?"

"No, that was something else," she said. "Besides, the doctor told me it's only sprained. Fucking doctors!"

I looked through the clean desert air and breathed the warmth in through my nose, out through my mouth.

At her house, I opened the trunk and got the wheelchair. I lifted her from the taxi to the chair one more time and pushed her up the steep driveway toward the door. The sun glinted off the metal chair. My face was sweating. All I had to do was let go of the chair and she would roll backwards 30 feet into the street.

At the door, she said, "Sir, could you, could you..."

The dogs were barking inside. I turned around and left her there for them.

THIS SHIT KICKS VIAGRA'S ASS

My sunflower-yellow cab stopped in front of a small trailer on a gravel road. A big old man came slowly out into the sun, his body jerking and flailing with advanced Parkinson's. He had a cane when he really needed a wheelchair. His legs and feet went around in circles three times with each step. It took five minutes for him to climb into the passenger seat. The air conditioning was cranked. It was 108 degrees outside.

"That feels fucking good," the big old man said.

"Hot out there," I said.

"I'm Phillip," the big old man said.

"Matt."

We shook hands and he gripped me to stop the shaking.

"Be honest with me," Phillip said, a few miles down the road. "How old do I look to you?"

His face was not too beaten up and he had good skin and a shaved head.

"About 60," I said.

"I'll be 70 tomorrow," Phillip said.

"Happy birthday."

"I've got a date with Maria," he said, "a little gal I met the other night."

"Sounds good."

"You don't believe me?"

"I believe you."

"If you don't believe me, I'll call her right now," Phillip said.

He twitched and fidgeted with his cell phone, then dropped it on the floor. I bent down and got it for him.

"Thanks."

With much effort, Phillip managed to dial a number. He put it to his ear and kept looking at me and giving me that "you'll see" look. It rang and rang and rang.

"Well, she must not be home," he said.

I got him to his doctor and helped him inside. Then I drove over to the park to wait. I sat in the park watching the pigeons. The pigeons just pecked the ground and ate what was there. They always were eating. They slept in the trees and they ate what was on the ground. And there was no shame in that.

In an hour, I went back and picked Phillip up from the doctor. Everything looked bad. But there was a bright spot: the receptionist had given him some free samples of a new drug that was supposed to help a man achieve and maintain an erection.

"This shit kicks Viagra's ass," he said. "I'm gonna have one happy fucking birthday!"

Phillip wanted to stop at a hamburger place on the way home. I went in with him. Two steps inside the door, he fell jerking and spasming to the floor. He knocked a man's coffee out of his hand and lay there, looking up at me with a terrified look. It took three men to get him to his feet.

Then, at the counter, he didn't have enough money for what he ordered. The cashier called the manager over and the manager looked like he was terrified of some kind of legal liability. Phillip's head was bleeding a little bit, but he shook it off.

"I'm fine," he said. The manager gave Phillip his food for free just to get him out of there.

We made it out to the cab. Phillip couldn't believe his luck. He ate his hamburger as I drove him back to his little trailer in the dust. He shook my hand again and then staggered toward his trailer door.

"Happy birthday!" I hollered out the window.

Phillip stood there trembling and shaking all over. He grinned and lifted his cane to the sky.

AND DELIVER US FROM THE VIKINGS, AMEN

A flashlight comes on in the dark. The light defines the motions of a man's hand as he rises to his feet. The light lands here and there on empty liquor bottles, a ratty bed roll, chunks of concrete, dirt, and sand. He fumbles with his bed roll and his small bag of clothes, grunting and groaning and complaining in the cold morning air. He hides his belongings between two rocks and turns away.

He stumbles out into the rising sun and glares at the sky. He lowers his head and shakes it, rubs his eyes. He's 51, of substantial build, with a long red beard that comes to a point. Layers of filthy clothing hang on his body as if thrown there. He looks like an old, tired Viking. People have told him before that he looks like a Viking, and he likes the thought of it. But here, in the desert, there isn't much call for Vikings.

It's still early, but the heat of the desert city is already building.

There is a chain-link fence with a large hole in it and a sign that says "CITY OF TUCSON WATERSHED, KEEP OUT." The tunnels are dry this time of year and will stay that way until the monsoon rains arrive in a month. He'll need a summer home by then. He's made the mistake of sleeping in the tunnels too late into the season. Waking up in a torrent.

His fingers are thick and dirty as he rolls a cigarette from a yellow pouch. He brings the thin cigarette to his lips and lights it with a book of matches, singeing his red mustache. There's a clump of burned hair above his lip.

He climbs a rocky embankment to the city road and walks south past some apartment buildings. A yellow taxi comes flying along and nearly hits him. Mike gives him the finger as the taxi speeds away.

183

As he walks along, he laughs to himself.

It's Thursday. Every Thursday, he goes to see Mel's dogs. Mel owns Mel's Grocery and Mel's Laundry. Mel lives above the grocery, and out back he keeps two Rottweilers, one male and one female, in cages. Mel never bothered to name the dogs, so Mike named the female She. He didn't name the male. The male is just a big, dumb, empty head. But She is smart. Mike likes to play with her in the vacant lot behind the old Sears building. Just last week, they were playing ball. They huddled up.

"Okay, She," he said, "go out ten yards, make a left. I'll throw you the ball." She looked at him understandingly. "Got it? Okay, hut, hut..."

She sprinted 15 yards, turned to her left.

"No, no, no," he called, waving her back. They huddled again. She looked at him. "Now," he said, "I said TEN, didn't I? Go TEN yards, cut left. Okay? Break!"

This time, she got it right. He threw the tennis ball. She caught it gracefully.

Once, he tried this with the male. Not only had he failed to master any running routes, but he'd eaten the ball.

Mel never plays with the dogs. They fester in their cages, dirty, with nothing but the cement to sit on, their own shit piled up, hardly any shade, and their water full of dirt. Mel sometimes gives Mike old bread and throwaway items from his grocery, and so Mel isn't all bad, but the way he treats those dogs is no good. They need to run once in a while; animals need to run and to feel free once in a while or they just go crazy, or they get so depressed they might as well be dead. Some people just don't understand this, or they don't care.

He approaches the cage and only the male stands up. It walks with its big, dumb head over to the fence. His heart jumps. She lays on the concrete with two trickles of blood dried on her nostrils. Flies.

He opens the cage and goes in and bends over her. He kneels down and looks. The male, separated by a fence, stands and stares.

He thinks of his father-in-law, Stan, dead at 60, the only real friend he ever had. He remembers looking at him lying in the coffin, his harelip twisted up in death. He was buried in the Berryfield Cemetery. He goes there every year on the anniversary of his death and pours a beer into the dirt and sits for a few minutes.

He stands up and walks out of the cage and around to the front door of Mel's store. He goes inside the little old-fashioned grocery.

"Mel," he says. Mel stands behind the cash register reading the daily newspaper. He's 62 years old, bald. A television is on with the volume very low.

"Mike," Mel says.

"She's dead," Mike says.

"Yes," Mel says. "Yesterday. I was going to tell you when I saw you."

"You saw me yesterday," Mike says.

"I forgot," Mel says.

"You're just going to leave her there?" Mike says.

"I told the Benson kid to bury her," Mel says. "After he gets out of school today, he'll take care of it."

"How'd it happen?" Mike says.

Mel shrugs.

"Stroke, maybe."

"I'll bury her," Mike says.

"Let me give you something," Mel says, digging into his till for dollars.

Mike waves off the money.

He walks back. At the cage, he stands and looks at the male. The male stands there and he looks sad, but Mike doesn't think the beast has the ability to feel sadness or happiness. And then Mike feels very sorry for the male and bends down and tries to stroke its big, dumb head. The dog bends its head lower and lets out a small pitiful noise. Then he snaps at Mike's fingers, narrowly missing.

Mike picks up She in his arms. She is heavy and stiff and it feels strange having her there, the weight of her. He never thought to pick her up when she was living, doubting she would have allowed it. He carries her nine blocks to a place down by one of the dry washes. People stare at him, but people always stare at him. Along the side of the dry wash, near a favorite camp site, he lays her down. Then he sits down beside her to rest.

In his mind, his father-in-law is standing there, looking at him, smiling with that cleft lip. Old Stan. Mike married Stan's only daughter. Her name was Punk.

"Punk?" Mike said when he met her.

"Watch how you say that," Punk said.

This was before Vietnam. Before he was caught and beaten and stuffed for years in the dark cell. Before he was rescued and then thrown to the dogs of his own country.

He and Punk fell in love, had one child. Meghan. They still live across town. Punk hasn't allowed him to see Meghan, but the little girl knows of him. Last Christmas, he called her. There was a church over on 22nd Street where you could go and sleep and get a hot meal. They also had a telephone. Meghan told him she missed him and wanted to come and live with him. She was five.

"You can't come live with me," he told her.

"Why not, Daddy?"

"You wouldn't like it here."

"If you're there, I'd like it," she said.

He holds no hard feelings against Punk. He understands. He is too much like her father Stan. Neither could ever quite fit with the world.

Every chance they got, Stan and Mike would slip off and go fishing.

"How much work you got today?" Stan would say. Mike would check his list to see how many water heaters he was supposed to go repair.

"No emergencies," Mike would reply.

"Let's go fishing," Stan would say, with that funny way of talking because of the harelip: "Ess go fwishin!" And off they'd go. This was back in Jersey. They had a 32-foot boat. They would go to the liquor store to get the "bait" and then down to the oceanfront.

One day, they were out on the water. It was calm and not too cold and old Stan just lay back and went to sleep. That was fine with Mike; he just sat there and rolled with the swells. Well, pretty soon Mike got sleepy, too, and they were both asleep.

Mike woke up to the deep anguished cry of a large horn blasting from heaven. Stan was already awake, working his fool arm off on the outboard motor, YANK, YANK, YANK, like some kind of madman in a yo-yo nightmare. Above the frantic image of Stan loomed the biggest, blackest tanker ship Mike had ever seen. It was an unloaded oil tanker, headed straight for them. Mike looked up at the people on the railing of the tanker. It seemed a mile high. They looked like little toy army men with movable arms.

Mike and Stan made it out of the way, barely.

They had had some good times.

He opens his eyes and looks at She lying there. Then he crawls over to where the ground is softer and begins digging with his hands.

By the time he's through digging the hole, his face is shining with sweat. He stands up and gathers She into his arms again. The flies are crazy around her eyes. He sets her down gently into the shallow grave. Then he gets down on his knees again and begins pushing the dirt over her. He pours the dirt on top of her, stopping to spit as the dust rises into his mouth. The look of the dead dog makes him sick to his stomach. She finally disappears. He pats the dirt. He sits there and stares at the mound of dirt until the sunlight begins to fail.

When it gets dark, he gets up and makes a small fire. The fire lights easy. It hasn't rained in over 100 days.

Mike stares into the fire. What he sees is a fire on the edge of a cliff above choppy water. He strokes his long, red beard and thinks about the Vikings. He thinks about the dead they left in the water and the graves they left on tiny deserted islands. He thinks about those big wooden ships with the carved dragons rearing in front, cutting through the cold fog of the north seas, coming for him.

SOMEBODY SAY THE MAGIC WORD

I get out of the cab and step into the oven of a normal Arizona summer day. I can't find her, I can't find her. My passenger is supposed to be at the "hypnotism clinic" at 5499 N. La Cholla. The orders are clear on my computer screen: name, phone number, pick-up address, destination address, amount I will be paid. I look inside and I call out her name. Several people sit in the waiting room and they all turn their eyes to me as if asking for help, but no one stands up. I go to the receptionist window. No one there. Back outside, I look around the area. Sometimes they wander off; I find them hiding behind bushes. I dial her phone number once again, but it's the same mechanical female voice: "The number you have dialed is a non-working number, please check the number and dial again…"

I'm about ready to give up when I see a woman coming from around the outside of the building waving at me.

"Carol Dingee?" I say.

"That's me."

She is five feet tall, thin, maybe 55 years old, Italian descent. Her smile is like the smile of a real estate broker on a billboard. Brown pants, purple blouse. She carries a white purse that probably cost more my car.

I get behind the wheel of the cab and she gets in the back.

"Well, that was a waste of time!" she says. "They put me in a chair and put these little glasses on me and they attached two electrodes on the sides of my head. They had some music playing, too. I honestly don't know if I was hypnotized or not."

"No pocket watch on a chain?"

"I have driving anxiety. I can't drive, I just can't drive. Driving is too stressful."

She is on the free cab ride voucher system, which was designed to be a service for the severely disabled and elderly. But there are loopholes. I get paid either way. I'm part of the system.

"That's how I got on this ride program," she says. "At first, they were sending a van to pick me up, and I had to share the ride with other people. One time, I had to sit across from a guy who was picking his nose the whole time. Can you imagine?"

"I don't have to imagine."

"I had to sit there and watch him pick his nose. I was trapped there watching him pick his nose. It was absolutely disturbing. When I got home, I took off all my clothes and threw them away. I felt so dirty. I took an hour-long shower, and I called them up. I told them I don't want that van anymore, you send me a cab."

"We transport a lot of mentally challenged people. I'm sure he wasn't doing it to annoy you."

"Irregardless. God damned, they charged me 1,200 bucks back there at that place. What a bunch of quacks! I honestly don't know if I was hypnotized or not, I honestly don't know."

"Maybe you're still hypnotized? Maybe this is all a dream?"

"I just want to improve myself," she says. "I'm into self-improvement. I'm always improving myself. It's a habit of mine. I saw their commercial on TV. I thought, I'll try it. I'm open-minded."

Maybe I'm the one who's hypnotized? I think. Or maybe I'm insane? Maybe the narrative of my life is one long illusion? Maybe I'm actually strapped to a bed in a loony bin somewhere, drugged and drooling and picking my nose without true awareness?

She can't keep her mouth closed. She is addicted to the sound of her own voice. She rambles about everything under the sun: her dog, the quality of avocados, her husband's suicide, the weather, real estate, turn lanes, her son who lives in New York, her daughter who lives in Minnesota, Valium, the human brain, canaries, flat feet…

I think, *maybe they could do something about your motor mouth the*

190

next time they hypnotize you. I think, maybe your husband killed himself so he wouldn't have to listen to you yap anymore. I have these cruel thoughts sometimes. Voices in my head. Maybe they don't belong, but there they are.

…chicken breasts, Sweden, computers, garlic, the Arizona state bird (which she said was the road runner but is actually the cactus wren), the fact that men in Arizona don't shave right…

Maybe I should write a story about this? Life is confusing, that's all I know; life is very confusing and maybe writing about it would help. Writing as therapy, self-expansion. It is important for the main character to be changed at the end of a story. That is crucial, I had read that on the Internet. A person named Sharon wrote it in her latest blog post, "Nine Crucial Elements of a Successful Story." Like when a person goes to a clinic to be hypnotized, they should come out changed somehow, preferably improved. Two-dimensional characters who do not change: that's simply bad writing. Static. My passenger is $1,200 poorer, but for her, that is just a drop in the bucket, a twitch of an eye.

"Can you turn that radio down? I can't even hear myself think back here."

I turn down NPR. Thousands of Syrians are being hanged to death by their own government. Mexicans are picking heads of lettuce in Yuma. A dam is ready to bust in northern California.

"Those libtards don't know what they're talking about," she says.

…the incompetence of her gardener, cell phone service providers, the full moon, the new $10 bill, Wellbutrin, tile roofs, saguaro cacti, anxiety…

Anxiety, I think. How do you get rid of that crap? Having someone drive you around for free might be a good start, and someone to mow your grass and someone to hypnotize you and tell you everything's going to be fine. The main character of a story should fight his or her way through anxiety and come out the other side. There should be a struggle. I would like to ask Sharon about the issue of anxiety on her blog, but her comments have been disabled.

…hairspray, cosmetic surgery, shoes, Alaska, Gavi Italian restaurant (terrible), the Korean War, Trader Joe's…

A brand-new Mercedes swerves into my lane in front of my cab. I slam on the brakes. This is how people drive: like nutcases. Everybody's in a mad-eyed hurry to get to the next red light. Everybody is angry. One car-length ahead: victory! That's all people have, it seems; that's how they get through the day, that's what bolsters them, that's their purpose. A world of one-uppers. People relocate from places like Boston and New York to Arizona. You'd think they would come here to relax, to get away from the hustle and bustle of those places, but they just bring their spastic mentality with them. They bring their disease. And after a while, it rubs off on me. I'm infected. I start driving like that, too. Fuck you! I blow my horn! Let's GO, moron! I cut people off, screw the turn signal. We have everything, but it's never enough. Nothing makes any sense.

…night sweats, New Jersey, where she's from (couldn't have guessed), the beach, the internet, Fox News (only non-fake news on TV), coffee, airplanes, illegals, ISIS, turnpikes, Macy's, the fact that everyone speaks with bad grammar these days…

There comes a time when the protagonist in a story has to assert himself.

I say, "You mean like the president's grammar?"

That gets her. That's a line I shouldn't have crossed. Conflict is good. People enjoy conflict. I mean, people sitting comfortably reading a story enjoy conflict.

"I've never noticed anything wrong with Trump's grammar," she says. "And I'm good at English, I'm very good at English; if there's anyone who's good at English, it's me! I was a quick learner in school. Besides, look at what that OTHER guy did for the last eight years!"

She had been hypnotized after all.

"How'd we get on Obama?"

"You brought it up. I was just trying to have a conversation."

I ease up to a red light and sit there looking to my right at the man in the BMW. He is picking his nose. He won't look at me. It is like a face in a dream you think you recognize, but you can't be sure.

My cell phone rings.

"Pardon me, that's my wife."

"*Hola guapa.*"

192

"Hola, como estas? Ya llege a la casa."

"Bueno. Estoy bien, ocupado. Una vieja loca. Me cae gorda. Te llamo al ratito."

I hang up.

"What language were you speaking?"

"Spanish. My wife's from Mexico."

"Don't you think she should learn English if she wants to live in this country?"

"She does speak English."

"Then why were you speaking Spanish?"

"Because we want to. She's teaching me."

"How long have you been married?"

"Eight years."

"And she's just now getting around to teaching you?"

"She's been teaching me the whole time. It's hard."

"Is she teaching you real Spanish or some dialect?"

"They have certain words and expressions that are particular to Sonora, Mexico, but it's still Spanish."

"I mean, is she teaching you real Spanish? I took Spanish in high school."

"You didn't even recognize Spanish when you heard it."

"Sounded strange, that's all. Didn't sound like Spanish to me. Did your wife go to school?"

"When you hear someone speaking English from New Orleans or Australia, you can understand them, right? It's still English. Why don't you stop insulting my wife, how's that sound? How about some quiet time; you're almost home."

One tiny risk like that and I could lose my job. That's how it is nowadays. She could call my boss, tell them I was rude. That easy. I'm out of work, broke, fucked. The protagonist spirals out of control, ends up selling meth. The stories that have touched me most in my life are written by, or about, people who have dropped out of the rat race altogether, people who try to be as free as they can, who value freedom above all else. Of course, they always suffer for it. Oh, the balls that would require, to just say to hell with it, to hell with life in harness. But I'm too afraid, too timid. I had a dream the other night where I was driving my cab and there were two tigers running along beside me, two gloriously orange- and black-striped tigers just running along beside me. Dreams are confusing, almost as confusing as life.

"Hey, don't get the idea I'm a bigot!" she says. "It's just that they come here and they don't learn English. They speak Spanish in the stores because they don't want you to understand all the horrible things they're saying about you. It happens all the time!"

"Now, now, I'm sure that's not true."

"Well, I'm no bigot, if that's what you think! I happen to have a Mexican maid right now, and the last one was BLACK!"

Somebody snap their fingers. Somebody say the magic word. Somebody shake me. I drop her off at her $300,000 house, big American flag waving in the front yard, the landscape perfectly groomed. She's steamed. She's going to need a massage now, a nap, a cool towel on her forehead.

I drive away. I look at myself for a second in the rearview mirror. Am I changed? Does a bit more cynical count? Does 30 minutes older count? Does $11 richer count? Amateur stuff, not very significant or meaningful. Maybe I will need to add a fictional element to the story. Maybe some sex? Space aliens? A police shootout? Baby in an oven? Don't neglect to describe the environment. Sharon made that clear in last week's writing blog. The desert is there, stretched out beyond the fancy houses towards the mountains which are hunched in shadowed wrinkles, massive stone tigers with hatchet backs. What I really want to do is write a story that has eternity in it, a story that is not an escape from reality but a light within it, a story that is not a cage but a key. No traps, no tricks. But who could do that? The thought of it floods me with a sense of power, but every time I try to do it, I am handicapped with anxiety and the fear of failure and inadequacy. At least I am still alive and there is no mushroom cloud rising in front of me. That isn't much of an epiphany. Maybe in the split second while my face melts away from the force of a nuclear explosion, I experience what seems to be a cab ride with a crazy person, and this has been it, and the crazy person is me? Or the crazy person is God? Maybe my body is just a pile of black charcoal back there in the parking lot outside the hypnotist clinic? I sit at a red light in the traffic and look around. I give it a minute. I almost zone out. When the light turns green, I'm still here. And we all lurch forward.

ARIVACA

Debora Hunter, 389 W. Rillito Drive, is seven feet tall; her head eclipses the sun. She doubles over to get in my cab, her face a sad skull with cracked hide stretched over it, bony hands like giant spiders, knees that knock the dash, a smile like an unknown species.

I begin the drive to Arivaca, a tiny town two hours south, way out in the desert, where UFOs are seen each night, where time seems to stop, where there are javelinas as big as cows with tusks like saber-tooth tigers. On the drive, she tells me she camped out in the hills of Arivaca for twelve years in a tent, sequestered in that quiet, peyote desert, and it was the most wonderful time of her life. It was much better than her childhood, much better than any of the years since then. There was nobody around to judge her or laugh at her, the way she looked; just the sweet deer and rabbits, the netherworld sunsets, the fruits of nature, a hidden spring where she got her water, which she boiled to drink.

"I can't live like that anymore," she says. "I had to move into town when I got sick. I had to come here and live with all these people around. People are very cruel. I've been here for the last seven years and I've gone to every so-called expert doctor in town, but they haven't done anything except stick needles in me and suck me dry...but it's almost over now, my old doctor has been calling me, he finally found a cure."

I don't ask what is wrong with her. If people don't tell you, you don't ask them, in the same way that you don't ask someone in prison what they are in for, or someone just out of prison, either. Anyway, what's the difference? She is not long for this world; none of us are.

On the twisting road to Arivaca, the radio goes to static and I turn it off. We watch the countryside in silence. As I round a sharp turn, we come upon a caravan of tarantulas crossing the road, a couple hundred of them trooping along. I stop the cab, the only car as far as you can see, and we watch the little hairy army cross the pavement. You can almost hear their footsteps under the autumn sun; you can almost hear them humming a song. The cab shakes with a gust of wind and I get a chill down my back, despite the heat. Debora doesn't think it strange at all. She smiles beneath her glossy eyes.

While we wait, she points out a tiny shack in the distance, tells me it's the home of a dead gold prospector who still haunts the place.

"There's a road up a little ways, on the right, see it?" she says.

"Yeah."

"Don't ever follow that road."

When the last spider has blended into the weeds, we get moving again.

"It won't be long now," she says. She takes a deep breath and sniffs the air. "Isn't that wonderful?"

"Yes," I say. It is wonderful: creosote, sage, mesquite, the clean desert air, the burned blue sky, the faint smell of cattle, jackrabbit fur, dry grass.

I've never been to Arivaca before, but I've heard rumors. Rumors about wild bulls fighting in the streets, Indians that never die, animals nobody's ever seen anywhere else. When we arrive, it's damn near a ghost town. I drop her off at a rickety Western-style building with boarded-up windows and high weeds in the path to the front door. There is a stand of timber surrounding it, which is odd because most of the area is high desert that can't support any trees, except the short scrubby mesquites. But this area is wooded with tall pines because of a river that cuts through its heart, a river that is probably drying out now, like most rivers around here, a river that I can't see or hear but I know must be here.

Tarantulas march across my soul and I feel an itch somewhere deep inside me.

"Good luck with your doctor," I say. "Nice to meet you."

She pays me with what seems like the very last of her money and smiles. She even tips me, and I feel bad taking it and try to refuse, but she closes my hand around the bills with her huge bony hand and assures me

198

it's all right.

As I drive away, I see her lope across the dirt road away from the rickety building with the boarded-up windows. She is so tall she is like some skinny ghost floating above the road, her head lifting into the foliage, and then she disappears into the trees.

THE REST OF IT

It's a hot mid-afternoon and I stop my cab at Fry's to buy a chocolate bar for my wife. She always asks me to buy her a chocolate bar and I usually forget. But not today. A chocolate bar costs a buck 79 now; can you believe it?

I get back in my cab and go to pick up old Francisca Verdugo from kidney dialysis. The nurse wheels her out in a chair, which is not a good sign; they never wheel her out like that. The nurse says she's okay, just a little tired, *"poquita cansada la pobrecita."*

I trust the nurse. I'm tired, too. We get Francisca in the front seat of my cab. She is groggy and quiet on the drive to her apartment. I am too involved with my own thoughts, and by the time we get to her apartment, she is out of it, won't respond to anything.

"Panchita, wake up! *Despiertese! Ya llegamos!"*

She is laid out on the seat. My blood goes cold. Her son's phone number is written on the side of her bag. I call him; he shouts, "She's diabetic! She's got some glucose tablets in her bag!"

I frantically go through her bag but can't find them.

"I don't see them!"

"Shit," he says, "I'm on my way! Do you have anything to eat? Some candy or something?"

I remember the chocolate bar, a miracle. I break off a piece and feed it to her like a baby.

"Come on, *señora,* eat it, it's good..."

She eats a little, though she doesn't want to, like I am feeding her something she hates, like I am feeding her some bad dream. I wave my hand in front of her.

"Do you know who I am? *Soy yo, Mateo! Señora!*"

No response.

More chocolate.

That bitch at the dialysis center must have known! God fucking damn everything! Everybody passing the buck. I think about calling 911, but her son said he'd be right there.

Panchita's eyes roll around.

"*Señora,* come on, *andele,* don't give up!"

She murmurs, "Daniela..."

I have driven her to and from dialysis many times. She has told me over and over again about how her husband died 32 years ago from a broken heart when their daughter Daniela died as a child, how she continued living in Nogales alone, how her son left and came to the States where he worked and sent her money. She wouldn't leave her old home, her old memories. But when she got sick, her son brought her here to Tucson, where she lives, if you can call it living, like a wild spirit brought inside to die a ridiculous death.

"*Señora! Despiertese! No se duerma!*"

She rolls her head around

I squeeze her hand, give her more chocolate.

Pretty soon, her son shows up burning rubber in his jeep, pulls to a stop in front of my cab, gets out, runs up. He's got a little blood sugar test kit. He throws open the door, grabs her.

"Mama! *Ama!*"

He tests her blood with a red drop from her finger. The little meter says 34, which is low, very low. I think when it hits 20, you're dead. He gives her some orange juice. He's always got orange juice. He pats her old face, says, "Please God, *por el amor de Dios,* she'll be all right; *ama,* do you know who I am?" He keeps tilting her head back, pouring the juice in. "Come on, ma, come on, yes, that's right, *muy bueno,* some more, there you go..."

Little by little, *poco a poco,* she begins to come around, that twinkle starts to come back into her eyes, though she still has no idea what is happening. She looks at him, says, "Daniela..."

He massages her neck, head, arms, he shakes her, hugs her, cries. Shit, I'm crying too. He wipes his eyes on her shirt. She says, *"Que pasa?"*

We both laugh, relieved. He lets her recover a bit more, then stands up, helps her out of the cab. She's sweating; her back is all wet. He curses the nurses at the dialysis center, props his old mother up onto the hot, cracked desert sidewalk, thanks me again for all I did, thanks me for caring.

I thank God I have a woman who loves me, who nags me to buy her chocolate. My heart's still racing. Jesus Christ, this poor old Mexican woman and her 53-year-old son, poor Daniela, poor everybody.

I watch them walk slowly to the doors of her apartment building and sit there for a second with my hands on the steering wheel, the half-eaten bar of chocolate on the seat melting in the sun, half-eaten away like my life, 43 years old and still driving this stupid cab, overweight and worrying about diabetes myself, so many dreams unrealized, fighting remorse like a pit bull.

I start the motor up, go away from there. My shift is over. I drive home through the city, the city that is beautiful but getting less so. It seems like everybody is sick; sick or insane.

I pull into my driveway, get out, pat my hand on the side of the house, go inside. I give my wife the chocolate bar and look at her: she's such a sexy, healthy Mexican woman, still young. I tell myself she will never get sick, never die, never leave me. Time will never touch her.

She looks at the chocolate bar, laughs, and says, "What happened to the rest of it?"

BEAR HUNTING

The difficult thing about Mr. Cooper is the fact that he's 98 years old. He's five feet three and narrow as a bird in his gray cotton pants and blue flannel. He uses an aluminum walker and watching him move is like watching the seasons change.

It's hard to believe it's October already.

In tired agony, Mr. Cooper climbs into the front seat of the cab and gets as comfortable as possible on his frail old bones. His hands are twisted red claws and his left twitches sometimes, and when it does, he brings it up to his breast pocket. In his pocket lives a bottle of prescription medication, and when he feels the bottle, he is reassured and his hand lowers calmly back to his lap.

It's 11AM and the Tucson skies are blue and warm.

"Morning, Mr. Cooper," I say. "How are you?"

"Fair to middlin'," he says. "Nice weather, isn't it?"

"Better than Minnesota?"

Mr. Cooper was a high school math teacher in Minnesota in his younger days. His wife died many years ago.

"I lived in Minnesota for 65 years," he says.

I pull out of the driveway and tool through the old man's neighborhood. Simple red brick houses ho-hum along gently curving streets.

I stop the cab at a stop sign and Mr. Cooper and I watch a toddler walking down the side of the road in nothing but diapers. The road is otherwise deserted. The fact that he's a boy is apparent in the square wobble of his strut, the tousled hair, the fat little arms at the ready.

I pull up slowly beside him. The boy scowls at me through the sun.

"Hello there," I say.

He keeps walking. He's determined to get somewhere. I slowly inch along, hanging my arm out the window. Mr. Cooper strains to look.

"What's your name?"

"Randy," he says in a little boy voice, growling with irritation.

"Where's your mom, Randy?"

"Don't know."

"Where's your dad?"

He looks at me as if I'm wasting his time.

"Don't know."

"Aren't you scared to be out here by yourself?" I say.

"No."

"Where do you live?" I say, looking around for any sign of a parent. He narrows his eyes.

"Don't know," he says. He's wise to me. It's taken him an hour to break out of the house and he isn't about to be taken back home so easy.

Mr. Cooper leans toward me, listening to every word. He has a huge grin on his wrinkled face.

"Where are you going?" I say to the kid.

"Goin' bear huntin'."

"Bear hunting?"

"Yup."

"What?" Mr. Cooper says. "What's he doing?"

"He's going bear hunting."

"I think you forgot your gun," I say. "What are you going to kill the bears with?"

He stops walking. I stop the cab. He looks at me as if he's studying the

206

theory of relativity. Then he shrugs and keeps walking.

"Widda rock," he says.

"A rock?" I say. "How far can you throw a rock?"

He leans down and with his tiny, chubby hand picks up a small rock from the side of the road. He rears back, and with the whole of his 40-pound, three-foot-tall frame, hurls it toward the horizon. The rock sails about five feet and lands quietly. He looks at me to judge my astonishment.

"Good one," I say. He dusts his hands off and keeps walking.

"You know," I say, "I think I saw a bear up around this next corner, so you better be careful."

He stops again and looks up at me. His eyes are wide and his mouth hangs open. Mr. Cooper laughs his old man's tenor laugh and thumps his skinny knee. I wink at him.

Then we hear a woman shrieking.

"RANDY! RANDY! RAAANDYY!!"

She runs into the road, feathers flying, and swoops him off his feet. She glares at me.

"What are you doing out here, honey?" she says to him, hugging him and rocking him side to side.

"He was going bear hunting."

She doesn't respond, just turns and races back to her house with Randy in her arms.

I drive on.

Mr. Cooper smiles all the way to the grocery store. The grocery store is the only place Mr. Cooper ever goes.

I pull up to the grocery store and park by the sidewalk. I get out and get Mr. Cooper's walker out of the trunk and open his door and stand the walker there for him. He grips the walker with his gnarled red hands and stands up and slowly heads for the store's front door.

"Watch out for bears," I say.

"Will do."

One time, a few weeks ago, I was waiting for Mr. Cooper to come out of the store and I had to use the bathroom. I left the cab and went inside. Inside, I saw Mr. Cooper standing with his walker, which had a little basket hooked onto it; he was gazing at the deli with its hot yellow lights and good greasy smells. He looked carefully and happily at all the foods, the brown crispy fried chicken and the pink ham and black roast beef and the red and orange and green salads. He stood there and watched all the people pick out their favorites, nodding in affirmation each time. Mr. Cooper always spends at least 30 minutes in the store and he always comes out with the same thing: a small sack containing a box of saltine crackers and a quart of skim milk.

Today, I watch him inch across the walkway and disappear inside the grocery store. The meter clicks higher as I wait in the sun. Somewhere out there is a bear with Mr. Cooper's name on it, and one with my name, too. Another cab comes up behind me, so I turn my hazard lights on. The lights blink and blink until he gets the message and drives around me.

ACKNOWLEDGMENTS

Rosebud, Left Hand Waving, Bull, Zygote in My Coffee, Full of Crow, Zouch, Gloom Cupboard, Night Train, Fried Chicken and Coffee, Smokelong, Scissors and Spackle, Bastards and Whores, Pithead Chapel, Horror, Sleaze and Trash, Nerve Cowboy, Chiron Review, Work Literary Magazine, In Between Hangovers, The Broke Bohemian, Fictive Dream, Steel Toe.

ABOUT THE AUTHOR

Mather Schneider was born in 1970 in Peoria, Illinois. He has lived in Arkansas, Washington, and Arizona, and now lives in Mexico, which is not as glamorous as it sounds. His works can be found in hundreds of journals and web sites, many of which are defunct. He has had many jobs, none of them teaching, although he was a janitor at a community college for eight months. He is most famous for being a cab driver in Tucson for 15 years.

terrorhousepress.com

CPSIA information can be obtained
at www.ICGtesting.com
Printed in the USA
BVHW081118260921
617564BV00007B/227

9 781951 897222